The Blueprint Dictionary of Printing and Publishing

Also by John Peacock:

BOOK PRODUCTION
THE PRINT AND PRODUCTION MANUAL (WITH BERRILL, BARNARD)

Also by Michael Barnard:

MAGAZINE AND JOURNAL PRODUCTION
INTRODUCTION TO PRINT BUYING
INSIDE MAGAZINES
MAKING ELECTRONIC MANUSCRIPTS
THE POCKET GLOSSARY OF ADVERTISING TERMS
THE POCKET GLOSSARY OF PRINTING, BINDING AND PAPER TERMS
THE POCKET GLOSSARY OF DESIGN AND TYPOGRAPHIC TERMS
THE PUBLISHER'S GUIDE TO DESKTOP PUBLISHING (WITH WILSON-DAVIES, ST. JOHN BATE)
THE PRINT AND PRODUCTION MANUAL (WITH PEACOCK, BERRILL)

The Blueprint Dictionary of Printing and Publishing

John Peacock
Michael Barnard

BLUEPRINT

First published in the United Kingdom, 1990

Blueprint Publishing Ltd
40 Bowling Green Lane
London EC1R 0NE
Tel 01 278 0333

British Library Cataloguing in Publication Data
The Blueprint Dictionary of Printing and Publishing.
   1. Printing and publishing
   I. Peacock, John II. Barnard, Michael 1944 -
070.5

ISBN 0 948905 47 6

Production note: keyed in WordStar and translated to MacWrite using the MacLink conversion program. Pages made up in PageMaker on an Apple IIcx. Illustrations scanned in on an Agfa flat bed scanner at 300dpi.

Printed in Great Britain by Antony Rowe Ltd, Chippenham, Wiltshire.

Introduction

The printing and publishing industries thrive on nostalgia and – unlike many (less attractive?) trades – their largely shared and somewhat esoteric vocabulary has until recently reflected historical tradition rather than the jargon of the computer-age technologists.

This is now changing, of course, and it is in the accommodation of this change that we have found the excuse to compile this dictionary. The encroachment of 'new' technology has enlarged and complicated the language spoken by publishers and printers and provided ever-increasing areas of semantic confusion. In attempting to embrace both tradition and technical innovation we have included terminology ranging from archaic mediaevalisms to technocratic jargon. But we think this is the nature of the current trade vocabulary and have had little hesitation in including both **minion** and **mips**.

We have also been prompted into this compilation as a result of a wide range of comment (thankfully mainly constructive) from our friends and colleagues in the industry who have pointed out errors of commission and omission in our earlier reference manuals and glossaries and have more generally bemoaned the absence of an up-to-date dictionary for the trade. For them in particular we hope we have produced a satisfactory solution.

We have borrowed several definitions from our shorter published glossaries – in particular those in *Book Production* and *The Print and Production Manual* – but have expanded many of these and of course added many more.

We have set out to produce a useful reference book for people working in the trade, rather than anything more academic. Where there is debate about precise definition of a term we have opted for common usage. Our intention is to enable the reader to understand *what the trade generally means* by a term and by and large we have not gone into discussions of derivation or examined grammatical variants.

Our ambition is to see dog-eared copies in publishers' offices and inky-finger-stained copies in printers' production departments.

Naturally, the book is imperfect. We (and the publishers) anticipate future editions so we would welcome your comments and additions.

JP

MB

Acknowledgements

We are most grateful to Blueprint Publishing, who allowed us to use material from some of our earlier books and made available a wide selection of illustrations which have helped to explain terms and add interest to the text.

We are also indebted to the many friends and colleagues who have helped with research and informed comment.

A

A The **A series** is an international **IS0** range of paper sizes reducing from 4A at 1682 x 2378 through AO at 841 x 1189 to A10 at 26 x 37, with subsidiary RA and SRA sizes. Each size folds in half to preserve the same proportions of 1: √2 at each reduction (see illustrations overleaf). See also **B, C**.

AAs Author's alterations. See **author's corrections**.

abbreviated addressing In computing, a process which enables a programmer to use an **address** that has fewer characters than the full address, providing a faster means of processing data as the shorter address requires less decoding time.

abort Controlled termination of a processing activity in a computer system.

above the line In publishing promotion and advertising, **above the line** activities include the production of catalogues, brochures, mailings, etc.which can be specifically identified with a particular title or list and charged to it in a promotion budget. As distinct from **below the line** activities, which include PR, author promotion, corporate or list promotion, etc, where costs can be less precisely allocated to projects.

abrasion resistance Measured resistance of a material surface such as paper to abrasion.

abridged edition A shortened version of a book.

absolute humidity Quantity of water vapour in a unit volume of atmosphere. Compare **relative humidity** (q.v.).

absorbency The degree in which paper takes up contact moisture. It is measured by a standard test.

absorption Absorption or **penetration** is one of the four principal ways in which inks dry; it is associated most readily with cold-set web-offset printing on newsprint. The other three methods are **oxidation, polymerisation**, and **evaporation** (q.v.).

abstract A short resume of an article in a book or journal which sums up the main points. Very common in **STM** publishing.

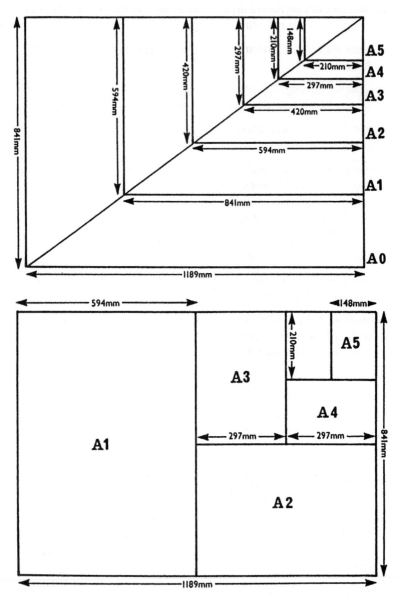

Illus 1 and 2. The A series of paper sizes. Top: the progressive reductions from A0 down to A5. Bottom: each size has its sides in the same ratio of 1 :√2.

accelerated ageing Testing of paper to determine strength loss through ageing.

accelerated drying Forced drying by one means or another, whether radio frequency, infra-red, ultra-violet, gas oven, etc.

accents Marks added to letters in some languages to indicate stress, e.g ´ in French.

acceptance testing The process by which a manufacturer tests a new system to demonstrate that it is in working order. See also **beta test**.

access The ability to retrieve data from a computer storage medium or peripheral device.

access control 1. The control system in computer networking imposed by **hardware** and **software** controls. 2. The controlled use of database information in such a way that restrictions may be imposed on the data items available and the operations that may be performed.

access fee Fee charged by a museum or gallery for the facility of photographing items in its collection. Also called a **facility fee**.

access time The time taken to retrieve data from a computer storage medium or a peripheral.

accordion folds Parallel folds in paper with each fold in an opposite direction from the preceding one. On completion the paper opens out like an accordion bellows.

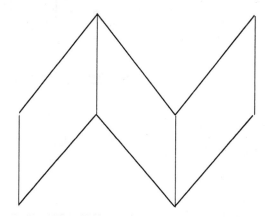

Illus 3. Accordion folds.

accumulator A computer store location for arithmetical calculation.

ACE Acronym for **ASCII Coded Escapement**. A typesetter **driver** language developed by Chelgraph and Monotype, and used in a number of photosetting machines.

acetate Cellulose acetate, a transparent film made from acetic acid and cellulose. As an **acetate overlay** it is used as a stable overlay material for fixing registered paste-up work over baseboard camera-ready artwork.

acetate proofs Acetate sheets, available in different colours, which can be developed and used as pre-press proofs. Also called **colour overleaf proofs**. See also **Cromalin, Matchprint, plastic proof**.

acetone Fast-drying solvent used in printing.

achromatic separations Colour separations produced by **CCR (complementary colour removal)**. The black printer carries more detail than with conventional separations and the tertiary, or complementary, elements of any colour hue are removed. Also called **ICR (integrated colour removal)** or **GCR (grey component replacement)**.

acid-free paper Generic term to describe paper whose furnish is free from acid-producing chemicals, and especially alum sizing, which reduce longevity. See **permanent paper** and **neutral sized paper.**

acidity Acidity is measured on a **pH value** scale in which pH7 is neutral; pH values lower than 7 indicate progressive acidity; and pH values higher than 7 indicate progressive alkalinity. The pH value scale is a logarithmic scale to the base 10, and so each unit differs from the next by a factor of ten. A substance with a value pH4 is ten times as acid as one of pH5, and 100 times as acid as one of pH6.

acid paper A paper which is not **acid-free** (q.v.). The sizing agents used will typically be the mildly acidic **alum** and **rosin** formulation (q.v.), and the **fillers** or coatings used will include inert **clay**.

acid resist Acid-resisting coat applied to a letterpress block or plate. It is applied in local retouching while a plate is being chemically etched in order to protect the non-etch areas.

ACK See **acknowledge**.

acknowledge In data communications, a character transmitted by a device as a response to a signal from another device to acknowledge that a connection has been achieved.

acknowledgements page Page of a book in which the author gives his list of sources and references.

acoustic coupler A transmission device similar to a simple **modem** which can be coupled to a standard telephone handset to allow the transmission of signals from one computer to another using the public telephone network.

across the gutter Printed over the **gutter** (q.v.) margin of a book.

acrylic A thermoplastic polymer based on synthetic resin and used for surface coatings among other applications. Acrylic coatings are tough, stain-resistant, flexible and waterproof.

ACs Abbreviation for **author's corrections** (q.v.).

action cycle In computing, the complete action, including origination, input, processing, output and storage, performed on data.

active file In computing, a file that has an expiry date later than the job date.

activity loading A method of storing records in a file which allows the most used records to be located more readily.

ad Advertisement.

AD Air Dry. Refers to the standard 10% moisture level of pulp.

adapter In computing, an **add-on board** or other plug-in device which provides support for additional facilities: more memory, more communications capabilities, more network facilities, etc.

ADAR Air dried all rag paper. A very superior and expensive paper for speciality use.

ADC See **analogue-to-digital converter**.

addendum Late addition to book after printing, often as a pasted-in slip. Compare **erratum slip**, **corrigenda**.

adder In computer architecture, the device that compiles an output from the sum of two or more input numbers.

additive primaries Red, green and blue, which when added together as light appear as white. Known also as the **light primaries**. Their complements or 'opposites' are known as the **light secondaries**: each one is made up of two colours out of the three, taken in turn. They are cyan (ie, minus red), magenta (ie, minus green), yellow (ie, minus blue). See illustration overleaf.

additives 1. Substances added to ink to control such performance characteristics as covering power, drying, permanence, etc. 2. **Loadings** and **fillers** added to a pulp furnish to produce specified qualities in a finished paper.

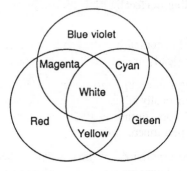

Illus 4. The additive mixing of coloured light.

add-on bar code A supplementary bar code used to encode information additional to that in the main code – typically price.

add-on board An expansion board (or card) that is inserted into one of the computer's expansion slots to provide additional features such as additional memory, communications, graphics, etc.

add-on device See **peripheral**.

address The character or string of characters identifying a unique storage location in computer memory or backing store.

addressability In computer graphics display, the number of addressable graphics points within a defined display or image area.

address field The particular portion of a computer word containing either the address of the **operand** or the information required to derive that address.

address format The arrangement of the parts of an address to identify a **sector** or **track** on a magnetic disc.

addressing 1. The assignment of addresses to the instructions in a program. 2. The communications method by which the originating unit selects a device to which to send a message.

Addressograph Proprietary name of a machine which uses individual plates to print names and addresses.

address track A track on a magnetic disc containing the addresses of files and records stored on other tracks of the same disc.

adhesive binding Binding style for books and magazines involving the application of a **cold-melt** or **hot-melt** adhesive to the roughened or ground back of a book to hold the pages and cover together. Also called **cut-back binding, perfect binding, thermoplastic binding, threadless binding.**

adjacent channel In computing, the communications channel in closest proximity, physically or electrically, to the one in use.

adjust An editing feature in word processing by which the processing software automatically adjusts the right-hand margin for the insertion or deletion of copy during playback and by which **word wrap** is automatically performed.

Adobe American corporation, inventor and developer of the PostScript **page description language** and PostScript-interpreting hardware. Adobe currently licence PostScript technology to a large number of OEM suppliers for use in the development of PostScript-encoded founts and in the **RIP** component of their laser printers and imagesetters.

Adobe Illustrator Adobe's popular DTP drawing package, often compared with the **Aldus Freehand** package.

advance The money paid by a publisher to an author in advance of publication of his book. The author's **royalties** on the book's sales are then set against his advance.

advance copies Early copies of a book sent by the binder to the publisher ahead of the main run for checking or for the publisher's use in early promotion. Also, **early copies, earlies.**

advance feed Sprocket holes in paper tape which align with code hole positions to indicate start of tape.

advance sheets Folded and collated sheets for the publisher's approval before binding.

aerograph See **airbrush**.

AFNOR Association Française de Normalisation. The French national standards organisation, similar in constitution to **ANSI** in the US or **BSI** in the UK.

against the grain Folding or cutting at right angles to the grain of the paper. Contrast **with the grain.**

agate 1. Obsolete term for $5^1/_2$-point-type. Also called **ruby**. 2. Standard measurement of advertising columns: 14 agate lines = 1 column inch.

air bar Bar on a web-offset press which conveys the web of paper. Tiny holes in the bar 'float' the web on a minute cushion of air, preventing set-off. A modern development from the **grater roller** which transfers the web by physical contact (and sometimes leaves patterns of smudges and set off: see **nutmegging**).

airbrush Small compressed-air gun used for fine manual ink spraying or retouching on artwork, photographs, etc.

air consignment note See **air waybill**.

air dried paper Paper dried by passing the web through warm air with only minimum support rather than on steam-heated cylinders. Sometimes used for limited-edition high-quality production.

air-dry pulp Pulp with a standard moisture content of 10%. See **AD**.

air gap The narrow air gap between a magnetic **read-write head** and the disc surface.

air knife coater Device which applies a jet of compressed air to the coating on a web of paper to achieve a smooth level film while fluid. Compare **blade coater**.

air knife cooling The cooling of a heat-set web of printed paper using jets of compressed air.

airmail Lightweight paper, usually below 40gsm, used for stationery when postage cost is critical. Often coloured pale blue.

air shear burst Break in paper reel caused by trapped air.

air waybill Air-transport term for the document made out on behalf of the sender as evidence of the contract of carriage by air freight. Also called an **air consignment note**.

albumen plate Lithographic printing plate coated with albumen dichromate.

alcohol damping The use of alcohol in the **dampening solution** of a litho press. Alcohol has a lower surface tension than water, and is effective as an additive in transferring a fine layer of solution evenly to the printing plate.

alcohols Solvents used in some inks.

Aldus American corporation, most famous for its software package **Page-Maker**, one of the foremost page make-up packages associated with the Apple Macintosh and DTP. PageMaker's main rivals are **Quark**

XPress and **Ready,Set,Go!** (q.v.).

Aldus Freehand A popular DTP drawing package.

ALGOL Algorithmic Language. A computer **high-level language** used mainly for scientific and mathematical applications.

algorithm An arithmetical computer routine in the form of programmed instructions which performs a recurring task.

algorithmic language A language specially designed for expressing algorithms such as **ALGOL**.

align To line up type horizontally or vertically using a typographical criterion, e.g. **base alignment** (q.v.).

aligning numerals See **lining figs**.

alkaline paper An **acid-free** paper with a residual reserve or buffer of extra alkalinity: the sizing agents used will typically be synthetic, neutral sizes, and the fillers or coatings used will be chalk (alkaline calcium carbonate) rather than clay.

alkalinity The opposite of **acidity** (q.v.).

alkali resistance Quality in paper which resists staining or discoloration by alkaline materials.

alley Space between columns of type on a page (US).

allotter Computer device which directs files to specific peripherals.

alloy Composition of several metals.

all rag paper Paper made from rag pulp.

alphabet A set of all the characters, digits and symbols used in a language or work. A set of the characters used in a code language such as **ASPIC**.

alphabetic character set One which contains letters but not digits, but may contain control and special characters. Contrast **alphanumeric character set**.

alphabetic coding Abbreviations used in the preparation of information for input into a microcomputer allowing information to be reported in the form of alphabetic characters as well as numerics.

alphabetic shift The key or control for selecting an alphabetic character set on a alphanumeric keyboard.

alphabet length The length of a lower-case type fount. Used by Linotype as a basis for their cast-off tables.

alphanumeric Relating to the full alphabetic and numeric character set of a machine.

alphanumeric character set A complete alphabet of alphabetic characters and numerals, as well as the normal control codes.

alphanumeric sort A computer sort of items into alphabetical order.

alpha test The testing of a software package prior to a **beta test** (q.v.).

ALU Acronym for **arithmetic logic unit**. In computer architecture, that part of the central processing unit (**CPU**, q.v.) in which arithmetic and logical operations are carried out on the data provided.

alum Aluminium sulphate. One of the main components in papermaking **size** (q.v.) and used in combination with **rosin** (q.v.). Alum is a mildly acidic substance, and cannot be used in the furnish of **acid-free** papers.

amberlith Proprietary name for an orange acetate sheet with a peelable coating, used to make light-proof masks when assembling films.

ambient conditions Those conditions pertaining to the surrounding medium (temperature, noise, etc.).

ambient noise level In computing, a random and uncontrollable noise level in an electrical circuit. See **noise**.

American Standard Code for Information Interchange Abbreviated to **ASCII**. A data transmission coding standard designed to achieve compatibility between data devices. Each symbol in ASCII code consists of 7 data bits and one **parity bit** for error-checking purposes. This combination allows for 128 code combinations. If the eighth bit is not used for parity checking, a total of 256 code combinations is possible, known as an **extended ASCII** set.

ampersand The symbol '&' meaning 'and'.

analogue computer A computer which represents numerical data by analogous physical variables such as speed, length or voltage rather than by digital representation. Contrast **digital computer**.

analogue-to-digital converter (ADC) A device which produces digital output from an analogue input. Compare **digital-to analogue converter**.

analyse scanner or **analyse unit** The input half of a colour scanner which scans the original and takes the scanning signals into memory. As distinct from the **output scanner**, which is the half that records the scanned signals on to film creating the separations.

analyst In computing, a person who defines problems and suggests procedures for their solution.

anamorphic scaling Scaling in which one dimension of a subject is reduced or enlarged to a different proportion from the other dimension: for example, a halftone reduced 30% across the width and retained at original size in the depth.

AND In computing, a logical operation in which, for example, A AND B has a true result only if both of the variables A and B are true.

and gate Computer function interpreting the concept **AND** in program code.

angle cutting Web sheeting at an angle rather than cutting horizontally to the machine direction.

Anglo-American system The system of printer's measurements used in the USA and Britain based on the **point** of 0.013837 inches and the **pica** of 0.166044 inches. Compare the **Didot** system.

aniline ink Volatile ink which dries very quickly. Used in **flexography** (q.v).

aniline printing Obsolete name for **flexography** (q.v).

animal glue A gelatinous and high-tack glue made from animal hides, hooves and bones. It is used extensively in casemaking. See also **starch paste**, **PVA**.

annotate To supply additional comments to the text of a book.

annotation symbol A symbol used by a programmer to append messages or notes to a **flowchart**.

anodised aluminium Aluminium treated in an electrolytic bath so that it resists oxidation with the air. Most conventional litho plates are made from anodised aluminium.

ANSI American National Standards Institute. US standards co-ordinating body similar in constitution to the **BSI** (British Standards Institution) in the UK. Other prominent national and international standards bodies include the **DIN** (Deutsche Industrie Norm) in Western Germany; the **AFNOR** (Association Française de Normalisation) in France; the **JIS** (Japanese Institute for Standards) in Japan; and the **ISO** (International

Organisation for Standardisation) as the internationally accepted co-ordinating body.

answer In publishing, the status response given to a bookseller or other buyer when the publisher cannot immediately supply the book the buyer requires. Typical answers include O/P (out of print); R/P (reprinting), often given in conjunction with a date for availability; N/K (not known) for mistaken identity; and several others.

anti-halation backing Coating on the back of photographic film which prevents halation.

anti-oxidant Ingredient in an ink which extends the **open-time** of an ink on press.

antique A printing paper with a rough finish but good printing surface valued in book printing for its high volume characteristics. Also called **antique wove, book wove.**

anti-rust paper Paper with additives which protect metal surfaces against rusting.

anti set-off spray Fine spray sometimes applied on printing machines at the delivery end to prevent **set-off** (q.v.).

anti-tarnish paper Paper with additives which protect bright metals against tarnishing.

aperture Lens opening on a camera, expressed as an **F number** (q.v.).

API American Paper Institute. US co-ordinating body for the paper industry.

APL In computing, a powerful algorithmic language employing an extensive set of data structures and operators.

APL terminals Range of popular input and editing terminals supplied by Linotype as a standard **front end** system.

apochromatic Lenses which focus blue, green and red in the same plane.

apparent density Weight of paper per unit of volume.

apparent specific gravity See **apparent density.**

appearing size The physical size of a type, as opposed to its nominal point size. Two type faces of the same point size can have very different appearing sizes.

appendix Addition to a book or document following the main text.

Apple Macintosh Family of microcomputers pre-eminent in **DTP** applications. In roughly ascending order of capabilities the present family comprises the 16-bit Mac Plus, Mac SE and Mac Portable, all running with the Motorola 68000 **chip** (q.v.); followed by the 32-bit Mac II, running the Motorola 68020 chip; and at the top of the range the Mac IIx, Mac IIcx and high-speed Mac IIci all running the advanced 68030 chip. Processing speeds vary from the entry-level Mac Plus at 7.3 **MHz**, up to the Mac IIci at 25Mhz.

application Use for a computer or computer system in accomplishing a task or solving a problem.

applications package A suite of computer programs used to solve problems specific to a particular area of endeavour: business, financial, scientific, for example.

applications program A program written to accomplish a specific task (such as word processing), as opposed to administrative or utility programs.

applications software Programs which are applied to solve specific problems, such as business systems.

approval copy A copy of a book sent to a teacher or lecturer for perusal and recommendation to his school or to his students.

APR Asahi Photosensitive Resin. Proprietary Japanese brand of letterpress **photopolymer plate** (q.v.). Widely used in massmarket rotary paperback printing.

aquatint Type of print using 'mottled' areas designed to resemble watercolour painting.

aquatone Form of **collotype** printing (q.v.) using a fine-screen gelatin-coated plate and offset printing.

arabic figures The numerals 1,2,3,4, etc. as distinct from the Roman I, II, III, IV. Evolved from Arabic symbols. Arabic figures can be typeset as **lining** or **non-lining** figures (q.v.).

architecture The design or arrangement of components in a microprocessor or other computer.

archival paper A paper with long-lasting qualities, usually with good colour retention. See also **permanent paper**.

archive To store data economically off-line for future use in a computer system. Compare **backup**.

arc lamp Lamp that produces light by a current which arcs across two electrodes, usually of carbon (thus, carbon arcs). Used as a light source in photography or plate-making.

area make-up Bringing together text and graphics into a page or area layout.

area storage A buffer of storage reserved for live data en route between a peripheral and its storage destination in a computer.

arithmetic logic unit See **ALU**.

array A series of items arranged in a meaningful grid pattern. In many programming applications, the term is taken to refer simply to an area set aside to store program data.

art Abbreviation (US) for **artwork**.

artboard Woodfree board coated to a high finish for fine printing of half-tones.

art canvas Loose wove, strong cotton with a tissue lining. Used in bookbinding.

artificial intelligence The ability of processors that can perform functions normally identified with human intelligence such as reasoning, learning and self-improvement in such a way that a device can improve its own operation.

artificial parchment A paper which simulates parchment.

art paper Paper coated with china clay and polished to a high finish.

art platen Letterpress platen printing machine used for proofing or printing half-tones.

artwork Original illustrative copy or typesetting ready for reproduction at pre-film stage.

Artype Proprietary name for a make of transfer type (q.v.).

ascender That part of a lower case character which extends above the **x-height** (q.v.). As in b,d,f, etc. See also **descender, extenders**.

ASCII Acronym for **American Standard Code for Information Interchange** (q.v.). The computer industry's standard coding system for data capture: each character comprises 7 or 8 information bits and one **parity bit** for error checking. Used by most word processors and the IBM-PC and compatibles, but not by IBM mainframes which transmit in

EBCDIC.

ash or **ash content** The residue of paper after incineration, gauged by standard test. Represents the amount of **loadings** and **fillers** (mineral content) that there are in the paper. Uncoated papers generally contain between 5-10% ash, coated papers up to 30%.

ASPIC Acronym for Authors' Symbolic Pre-press Interfacing Codes: a basic typographical coding system for the **electronic mark-up** of text, designed to be used by authors or their typists in preparing manuscripts for typesetting. It consists of a number of mnemonic tags, typed between square brackets, that are inserted at 'switching points' within the text to define the format required. These tags can then be converted into typography by the output photosetter or other device.

Headings		**Fonts**	
[h1]	*Starts first level heading	[r]	Roman
[1x]	Ends first level heading	[i]	Italic
[h2]	Starts second level heading	[b]	Bold
[2x]	Ends second level heading		

Text		**Paragraph endings**	
[t1]	*Starts first level text	]]	New para, without indent
[t2]	Starts second level text	[ ]	New para, with indent

Illus 5. Some of the basic ASPIC codes.

ASR Answer Send and Receive. Machine which can send to and receive from a computer by paper tape.

assembler A computer program which converts a **low-level language** into **machine-code**. Compare **compiler**, which rewrites a **high-level language** program in machine-code.

assembler box Part of a Linotype or Intertype linecasting machine in which the line is assembled.

assembly Bringing together pieces of film to make up rows of pages and produce final imposed **foils** for platemaking. Also called **planning** (q.v.).

assembly language A low level computer language which needs an **assembler** (q.v.) to translate it into machine code.

asterisk Star-shaped symbol (*) often used as a footnote reference mark.

asynchronous A mode of data transmission typically used for interactive transmissions, and the main mode used in the data communication of word-processor and typesetting files between micros ('comms'). The start and end of each block of data is signalled by start and stop **bits** rather than by any time relationship. Compare **synchronous** transmission (q.v.) where the signals are co-ordinated at each end by synchronised timing pulses.

asynchronous computer A digital computer in which automatic progress from one operation to the next is controlled by signals indicating that the previous operation has been completed.

asynchronous multiplexer A **multiplexor** device which provides an interface for up to 16 peripherals (terminals, printers, keyboards). Programmable functions include parity checking.

ATS Animal Tub Sized. Paper sized after manufacture with animal gelatine.

author-date A bibliographical reference system comprising the author's name and date of publication, e.g. Brown, 1984.

author's corrections Also, **ACs, author's corrs.** Corrections made by the author on proofs and changing the original copy as distinct from **printer's errors** or **literals** (q.v.) made by the typesetter. Author's corrections are by convention marked in blue; **printer's errors** or **literals** are marked in red.

autographic transfer Method of reproducing hand-written material from a special hard-sized transfer paper by lithography.

autokerning See **automatic kerning**.

auto-leading In DTP, the insertion of default leading equivalent to 20% of the type size being set. Thus, a series of 10pt lines set with auto-leading will be generated at 10-on-12pt.

auto-lithography Drawing of original artwork on a lithographic printing plate.

automatic bootstrap loader In computing, a programmed set-up which allows system start-up from a variety of peripheral devices without the need to enter commands from a key-board.

automatic dialling unit A device (typically a modem), that is capable of automatically generating signals which correspond to the dialled digits of a call.

automatic error correction In data transmission, routines which carry out the detection and correction (usually involving retransmission) of transmission errors. The degree of correction will be dependent on the error checking codes employed and equipment configuration.

automatic feeder Device on a printing or folding machine which draws paper into the machine.

automatic heading The positioning of a heading on consecutive pages by means of a generic instruction at the start of a project. Common on modern page-make-up systems.

automatic imposition equipment See **projection platemaking equipment**.

automatic kerning or **autokerning** The ability of some photosetting output systems automatically to adjust the letter fit of certain character combinations in text so that spacing is kept visually even.

automatic pile delivery System on modern printing machines which jogs printed sheets into an orderly pile and gradually lowers the accumulating stack.

automatic programming Any technique employed to simplify program writing such as the use of an **assembly program** to translate a programmer's symbolic code into machine language.

automatic transfer press A web-fed press which allows make-ready to proceed on one set of plates while a job is still running on a second set. There is then no press stop when the new job starts.

autopaster See **flying paster**.

autopositive film Photographic material which produces a positive image from a positive original without an intermediate.

autoreversal film Type of film used for making contact film duplication without requiring an intermediate stage of negative or positive, i.e. which will give a negative from a negative or positive from a positive. Also known as **direct-duplicating** film.

autosplice See **flying paster**.

auxiliary storage See **backing store**.

a/w See **artwork**.

azerty Keyboard arrangement used in France as alternative to the standard **qwerty** (q.v.) keyboard arrangement of characters. Accommodates **accents** (q.v.).

azure laid Blue tinted laid paper, usually used for stationery.

azure wove A paper like **azure laid** (q.v.) but without the characteristic laid lines.

B

B The **B series** is an international ISO range of sizes designed for large items (wallcharts, posters) and falling between the **A series** sizes (q.v.).

back 1. The binding edge of a book. The back margin is the space between the type and bound edge. 2. In binding, to form a shoulder on each side of the spine. See **backing, rounding and backing**.

back board The back of the case or cover of a book, as distinct from the **front board** and **spine**.

backbone US term for **spine** (q.v.).

back-edge curl Distortion of the back edge of a sheet of paper usually caused by heavy solids too close to the back edge. Also, **tail-end hook**.

back end In typesetting systems, the output device as distinct from the text-entry and text-manipulation hardware − the front end.

backer card Display card fixed to back of dump bin or stand.

back fold The fold in the centre of a book (ie, in the centre of its **back margins**).

background Computer processing mode which can occur concurrently with the main use of the machine, e.g. hyphenation and justification of a text file while other material is being input.

background processing Low-priority tasks, in a multitasking environment, that are performed when higher priority programs are inactive. In word processing, performance of a task such as printing while the operator completes other tasks.

background program One which does not depend on interaction with the user.

backing In binding, the operations which form a shoulder on each side of the spine. Also known as **jointing** (q.v.). In paper the carrier sheet for a peel-off stock.

backing store Mass storage medium on a computer, e.g. floppy disc, magnetic tape, etc.

backing-up See **back-up**.

back lining Strip of paper or fabric glued to the spine of a book to give reinforcement strength. See also **first and second linings**.

backlist The list of books which a publisher has in stock apart from his immediate **front-list** (current) titles.

back margin The margin of a book nearest the spine. See **margins**.

backmatter Alternative term for **endmatter**.

back number Copy of a previous issue of a periodical.

back-of-book Pages in a periodical following the editorial; often classified advertising.

backplane The wiring and connecting units that allow a computer to be connected to its peripherals.

back planing Method of reducing thickness of newly cast stereos by trimming the reverse side on a planing machine.

backs Combined **back margins** of a book.

back separation The action of an automatic stream-feeder by which the top sheet in the pile is lifted and forwarded from the back edge rather than the front.

backslant Backward sloping typeface, i.e. opposite to italic.

backslash A 45 degree downwards slash, '\'. As distinct from a forward slash or **solidus**, '/'.

backspace The movement of the cursor of a VDU or a printing head in a backwards direction along a line.

back swell A build-up of thread or glue at the spines of books during binding causing the spines to swell undesirably.

backup Operating system command to save selected groups of files held on **hard disc** on to **floppy disc**. See also **Restore**.

back-up The act of duplicating data for security purposes.

back-up ad Advertisement published in conjunction with an insert or editorial announcement.

back-up copy Copy of a working disc made for security reasons.

backward read A technique which allows a magnetic tape to be read while the tape is running backwards.

backwater Liquid containing dissolved ingredients in paper-making process, which passed through the wire when stock is deposited. Also known as **whitewater**.

bad break Undesirable end-of-line hyphenation of a word.

BAF Bunkerage Adjustment Factor. In seafreight, an extra charge added to basic scale charges to take into account the current cost of fuel.

bagasse Fibre sometimes used in paper-making obtained from sugar cane.

baggy paper Loosely wound web.

BAK A filename extension used by several **operating systems** to identify backup copies of files.

band A group of tracks on a magnetic disc. A communications frequency range between two defined limits.

banda A form of spirit duplicating machine.

band strapping Enclosing a stack of printed material with a strong, thin plastic band to secure it. The machine is a band strapper.

bank Grade of lightweight writing and printing paper from around 45gsm upwards used for correspondence, multi-part sets, etc. Weights over 60gsm are known as **bonds** (q.v.).

banner 1. Large headline on advertisement or newspaper story. 2. Poster or cloth strip containing an advertising message.

bar code Symbol defined by the European Article Number system which represents the **ISBN** of a book presented in standardised machine-readable form, and appearing in a defined position on the outside of a publication for stock control purposes. Add-on features can include the encodation of price.

Illus 6. A bar code containing ISBN and price detail.

baryta Heavy grade of coated paper sometimes used for reproduction proofs.

BAS A filename extension common to several **operating systems** denoting **BASIC** source program files.

base alignment Aligning characters of different sizes on the same line. See **base line, align.**

base artwork See **baseboard artwork.**

baseboard artwork or **base line artwork** Artwork presented on a stiff bristol board base with a tissue overlay indicating the colour splits.

base line Horizontal line on which characters in a line of type appear to stand.

base paper Paper to which a coating is to be added. Also called **body paper** or **body stock.**

BASIC Beginners All-purpose Symbolic Instruction Code. A widely used **high-level** computer programming language.

basic size American paper term for the specified sheet size used to define **basis weight** (q.v.). Different papers have different basic sizes: the basic size applied to book papers is 25" x 38".

basil Grade of leather produced from sheepskin and used in the production of account book bindings.

basis weight or **substance** 1. The weight of a material, usually paper, defined in grams per square metre. 2.(USA) Weight in pounds per ream of paper cut to **basic size** (q.v.). Typical US weights for book papers are 50lbs (equivalent to 74gsm), 55lb (equivalent to 81gsm), 60lb (equivalent to 89gsm).

bastard progressives Set of progressive proofs showing every possible colour combination of the four process colours.

bastard size Non-standard size of any material or format.

bastard title See **half title.**

BAT An operating system filename extension that denotes a batch file.

batch Method of computer processing where input data is collected into batches before processing, as distinct from **real time** or **interactive** operation (q.v.). A **batch pagination program** is one where the operator sets up the specificationparameters by using a menu, and then allows the program to make up the text into pages with no further intervention.

Contrast an **interactive page make-up program**, which requires continuous dialogue with the operator.

batter Broken or damaged type, blocks or plates.

battered Damaged printing surface.

battery-backed RAM A form of nonvolatile storage in which power is permanently supplied to memory modules even when power to the computer is removed.

baud Number of computer bits transmitted per second over a data communications channel. Typical rates of transmission range from 1200 baud (120 characters per second, or around 20 seconds for one sheet of A4 copy) to 9600 baud (960 characters per second, or around 3 seconds for one sheet of A4 copy). A typical baud rate for the data transmission of word-processor or typesetting files between micros is 1200 baud. As a very approximate guide to transmission times, the baud rate divided by 10 = characters per second. Alternatively, by a mathematical coincidence, the baud rate figure translates directly into words per minute (approximate).

baud rate See **baud**.

BCTMP Bio-chemi-thermomechanical pulp. A particular grade of **chemi-thermomechanical pulp** (q.v.).

bds Abbreviation for boards (ie, hardback).

beam splitter Prism system in a colour scanner which acts as a spectrum filter, splitting each light spot scanned into its **RGB** components following which each component is analysed inside the scanner's colour computer. A beam splitter serves the same function as do the red, green and blue filters in camera colour separation.

beard Distance from the bottom of the x-height of a piece of type to the bottom edge of the body.

bearers Hardened steel rings at the end of printing press cylinders.

bearer-to-bearer contact The principle of contact between the bearers of the plate cylinder and of the blanket cylinder, rather than the setting of a gap (bearer contact cylinders rather than bearer gap cylinders).

beater-sized pulp Paper-making furnish to which the size is added during beating rather than at a later stage in the process. See **internal sizing; engine sizing; sizing**.

beating Part of the paper-making process where fibres are mechanically treated in a **cone-refiner** (beater) to modify their characteristics to those required by the desired paper quality in manufacture. Also, **refining** (q.v.).

bed The flat metal part of a printing machine which holds the type forme during printing.

Bekk smoothness Measurement of smoothness of paper surface using the Bekk instrument.

bell A control character originally employed to ring a bell on teletype equipment. Now more commonly used to permit more codes than is possible from a six-level coding structure.

bell code Code permitting more phototypesetting commands than is normal on a six-channel coding structure.

below the line In publishing promotion and advertising, **below the line** activities include PR, author promotion, corporate promotion, etc, where costs are difficult to ascribe to specific titles or projects. Contrast **above the line** activities (q.v.).

belt press Printing press using two continuous belts for printing books in-line from a paper web to a delivered book, ready for binding at the end of the press. See **Cameron belt press**.

benchmark test A routine designed to evaluate the performance of a device under typical conditions.

Ben Day Mechanical process of tint laying now superseded by photo-graphic screen tints. Named after its developer, Ben Day.

Bendtsen roughness test Standard test to determine the surface roughness of a paper. The results are measured in millilitres of air which escape per minute from under a measuring head placed in firm contact with the paper surface. A typical reading for an 80gsm bond paper might be 400; smoother papers will have lower figures than this, rougher papers higher ones.

bespoke software Software written for a specific application for a single customer. Also, **custom software**.

beta testing The stage at which software is tested under real conditions, prior to general release. See **acceptance testing**.

bevel 1. Sloping surface of a piece of type between the face and the shoulder. 2. Outer edges of letterpress printing plate which are below type height and by which the plate is secured. Also known as a **flange.**

bf Bold face. See **bold.**

bible paper Very thin, strong, opaque printing paper used where low bulk, or weight, is needed. Originally made for bibles and prayer books, also used for dictionaries and air mailed publications.

bible printings Bible papers (q.v.).

bibliography List of books and articles relating to a written work, usually given at the end of the work. Each item in the list may include details of author, title, publisher, etc.

biblio page See **copyright page.**

bi-directional printing Movement both from left to right and right to left in a line printing machine (e.g. daisywheel printer) thus increasing output (conventional printing machines only move left to right).

bike To send materials by courier.

bill Poster.

bill-blade coated paper Paper coated on the paper machine using a particular form of **blade coater** which normally deposits around 10 gsm of coating per side.

bill of exchange A common payment instrument for exporters. It is defined as 'an unconditional order in writing, addressed by one person to another, and signed by the person giving it, requiring the person to whom it is addressed to pay on demand or at a fixed future time, a sum of money to a specified person, or to the bearer'. There are two basic kinds – the Fixed Date Bill, and the Sight Bill: a fixed date bill is paid on a due date, whereas a sight bill must be paid on presentation. Procedurally, once the goods are despatched, a bill of exchange is drawn up by the exporter and sent to his bank along with a set of ownership documents for the goods. The bank sends on the bill and documents to its branch in the buyer's country, and this branch contacts the buyer. In the case of a Fixed Date Bill, the ownership documents are transferred when the bill is accepted, but before payment is necessarily made; in the case of a Sight Bill, the ownership documents are only handed over when payment has been made.

bill of lading A statement of goods being carried by sea, used as a document of title by the consignor, and as a receipt by the shipping line.

bimetal plate Lithographic plate where the printing image area base is usually brass or copper, and the non-printing area is usually aluminium, stainless steel or chromium. Used for long runs.

binary Numbering system using the base 2 as opposed to decimal which uses the base 10. The only digits used are 0 and 1. In binary notation, decimals 0-15 for example are shown here:

		8's	4's	2's	1's
		(2^3)	(2^2)	(2^1)	(2^0)
0	is	0	0	0	0
1	is	0	0	0	1
2	is	0	0	1	0
3	is	0	0	1	1
4	is	0	1	0	0
5	is	0	1	0	1
6	is	0	1	1	0
7	is	0	1	1	1
8	is	1	0	0	0
9	is	1	0	0	1
10	is	1	0	1	0
11	is	1	0	1	1
12	is	1	1	0	0
13	is	1	1	0	1
14	is	1	1	1	0
15	is	1	1	1	1

Illus 7. Decimals 0 - 15 in binary notation.

binary counter A computer component comprising a series of bistable devices, or **flip flops**, each storing one bit of a **byte**.

binder 1. Device for holding loose-leaf sheets. 2. Person who does bindery work. 3. In papermaking, the chemical substance which adheres the coating of a paper to its base paper.

binder migration A condition in coated paper where the **binder** (q.v.) has dispersed unevenly and causes a mottled appearance in the printed image when printing is carried out.

bindery Place where binding is done.

binding 1. The process of fastening printed sheets together and securing them in a cover. 2. The bound part of a publication, i.e. cover, stitching, etc.

binding board or **binder's board** Board used in the covers of a case-bound book. Usually good quality and single-ply. See **case board, grey board, millboard, unlined chipboard**.

binding brass See **brass**.

BIOS Basic Input Output System: that part of an operating system that controls the interface with computer hardware.

bit Binary digit. A bit is the basic information unit in computer systems; each bit is either 0 or 1. A group of bits is known as a **byte**. A byte can vary in length, but typically 8 bits make up one byte for most microcomputing purposes. See also **binary**.

bite Stage in the process of etching a metal block or plate with acid. Each application of the acid increases the depth of the etch and is called a bite

bit map An array of **pixels** which together make up an image, either as a display on screen or as output to a graphics printer.

bit map fount A fount whose character descriptions are stored in the computer's memory as complete, 'solid', arrays of dots − one bitmap for each size used − rather than as instructions for building outlines (**vectors**) that can be used at many sizes and filled in by the computer when the image is drawn.

bit rate The speed at which data bits are transmitted over a communications line. See also **baud**.

bits per inch The number of bits recorded per inch of magnetic tape or disc track. See **bpi**.

bits per pixel See **bpp**.

bits per second See **baud**.

black and white Single colour black only originals or reproductions as distinguished from multi-colour. Sometimes called **mono** or **mono-chrome**.

black box Colloquial term for an electronic device which converts one type of input into another form of output.

blackening Loss of paper brightness in calendered paper where areas darken. Can be caused by paper being too damp when calendering is being carried out, or too heavy pressure.

black letter Also called **gothic**. A type style based upon a style of handwriting popular in the fifteenth century.

black printer The black plate in four-colour reproduction used to give correct neutral tones and detail.

black-step collation Method of ensuring sections of a publication are gathered in the correct sequence. The outer fold of each section is printed with a rectangle or short thick rule. The position of the rule on each section is such that when the spine of the complete publication is viewed, the rules form a stepped pattern. See also **collate**.

blad Sample pages of a book produced in the form of a booklet and used for promotional purposes.

blade-coated cartridge See **coated cartridge**, **blade coating**.

blade coater Machine or unit for **blade coating** (q.v.).

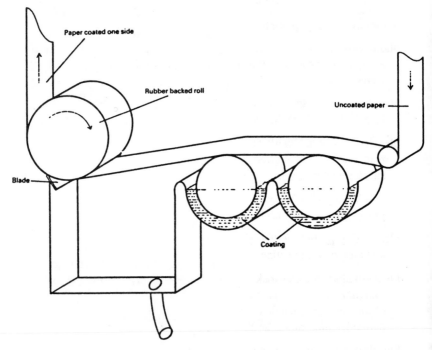

Illus 8. A trailing blade coater.

blade coating Paper coating method where a surplus of coating is applied to the web and then levelled and controlled by a flexible steel blade. Blade-coating can be done either on or off the paper machine (**on-machine** or **off-machine coating**.)

blade cut Paper defect where a **blade scratch** (q.v.) cuts deeply into the web.

blade scratch Paper defect where there is a hair-like indentation in a coated surface running in the grain direction. Caused by a particle lodged behind the blade during coating.

blade streak Paper defect which is similar to a **blade scratch** (q.v.) but larger and caused by a larger particle.

blanket A rubber-surfaced sheet clamped around the cylinder of an offset litho printing press which transfers the printing image from plate to paper.

blanket contamination Occurs where undesirable material becomes attached to the litho blanket and interferes with print quality.

blanket cylinder The cylinder around which the blanket is clamped.

blanket-to-blanket Printing configuration where two blanket cylinders act as opposing impression cylinders printing both sides of the sheet or web simultaneously.

bleached mechanical Grade of **mechanical** furnish paper which is strongly bleached to imitate the more expensive **woodfree** grades.

bleached softwood kraft One of the most common pulps used in the manufacture of woodfree offset printing papers. A form of bleached **sulphate** pulp (q.v.).

bleached sulphate Woodfree pulp made using the alkaline **sulphate** process (q.v.) and bleached.

bleached sulphite Woodfree pulp made by the acid **sulphite** process (q.v.) and bleached. In decline, due to environmental pressures.

bleaching Part of paper-making process where chemical treatment is used to purify, whiten, brighten and improve permanence of the pulp. The chemicals used include chlorine, chlorine dioxide, oxygen, hydrogen peroxide, magnesium bisulphite, and alkalis.

bleach-out Underdeveloped bromide print used as a basis for a line drawing. The bromide print is bleached away after the drawing is finished.

bleed Printed matter running off the cut edge of a page. The bleed allowance beyond the **trimmed size** is usually 3mm to ensure a clean cut-off.

bleed-back A condition when one printed colour feeds back into the ink roller train of a second colour when printing **wet-on-wet**.

blind 1. Blocking or stamping of covers or jackets without metallic foil or ink resulting only in an indentation or embossing. 2. Used to describe a litho plate where the image has lost its ink receptivity.

blind blocking Blocking or stamping of covers or jackets without metallic foil in order to smooth down, indent, or emboss the surface. Also called **blind stamping**.

blind keyboard Typesetting keyboard with no visual display (e.g. screen or marching display) or hard copy of keying.

blind stamping See **blind blocking**.

blind stitch The stitch which joins the books together in the sewing process. It is this stitch which is cut to separate one book from the next. See also **kettle stitch**.

blister Paper defect usually occurring during heatset drying of coated papers where clearly defined bubbles form on both sides of the web. Hence, **blistering**.

blister cut Paper defect resulting in a web cut often diagonal to machine direction.

blister pack Packaging method using a sheet of plastic holding bubbles of air which form a cushion of protection.

block 1. Etched copper or zinc plate used in binding for impressing or stamping a design on a cover. In letterpress, a plate which is mounted and printed with type. 2. Computer term for a group of **bytes** (q.v.) of information. 3. Any group of words or files treated as a unit.

blocking 1. Binding operation to impress a design or lettering into a book cover, often filling the impression with metal or pigment **foil**. 2. Fault where stack of printed sheets stick together as the ink dries.

blocking fee See **holding fee**.

block-pull Proof of a printing **block** (q.v.).

blottings Grade of highly absorbent papers.

blow-up To enlarge photographically; or a print so made.

blue key In film assembly, a form of key in which the image is produced photographically in drop-out blue, and is non-printing.

blueprints Contact dyeline proofs made on paper from film. Used for general checking purposes especially positioning. Also called **blues, bluelines, diazo prints, dyelines** and **ozalid prints**.

blues See **blueprints**.

blue wool scale Scale of light fastness for inks. 8 is the highest for printing inks. 6 is the minimum level required for exposure to daylight. Yellow and magenta inks tend to be less light fast than black and cyan.

blurb Brief description of a book, usually for the jacket.

board General term for paper above 220gsm (although sometimes applied to substances down to 200gsm). The term includes numerous grades ranging from those of one finish throughout, to those made from combining several plys of the same or different furnishes. Boards may be uncoated or coated one or both sides. See also **case board, paperboard**.

board hollow In case-making, a spine **hollow** (q.v.) made of the same board as the front and back boards. Used particularly in children's books.

body 1. Metal composing term for the solid metal of a piece of type carrying the printing surface. 2. Phototypesetting term for the size of the body of type, e.g. 12pt = a 12pt body. 3. Inkmaking term describing the viscosity of the ink.

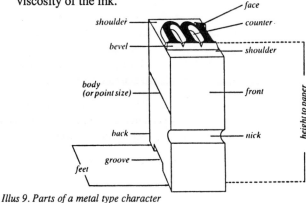

Illus 9. Parts of a metal type character

body copy or **body matter** Text pages as distinct from prelims, endmatter, index, etc.

body paper See **base paper**.

body size Same as typesetting term **body**.

body stock See **base paper**.

body text The main text of a book.

boilerplate text Sections of word processed text or of computer graphics held in memory for frequent retrieval and use.

bold or **bold face** Heavier version of a typeface, as distinct from light or medium. Sometimes abbreviated to **bf** (bold face).

bolt Folded edge of a printed section (other than the binding fold) which is removed in final trimming.

bond Range of printing and writing papers often used for letterheads, invoices, etc, in the substance range 60-100gsm. Similar papers of lighter substance (under 60gsm) are known as **banks** (q.v.).

bonded ink One suited to **hard-sized** (q.v.) papers, drying by **oxidation** rather than penetration.

bonded leather See **reconstituted leather**.

bonding strength Measurement of a paper's resistance to picking and delamination when printing.

book block Book at the binding stage after sewing or perfect binding but before **forwarding** operations have been carried out.

book club A subscription club for book buyers, often specialising in books on specific subjects, which offers its members titles at attractive discount rates compared with their normal retail selling prices.

book jacket Protective wrap-around to a book, usually made of paper.

book paper Paper with characteristics good for book printing but also used more generally.

bookplate Label intended to be pasted inside the cover of a book and bearing the owner's name, family crest, etc, for identification.

book proof Page proofs paperback-bound in the form of the finished book.

bookwork Production of books.

bookwove See antique wove.

boot or bootstrap Computer term for necessary instruction procedures where programs are loaded and activated prior to operating.

boot-up disc See **system disc**. Also, **start-up disc**.

borders Decorative designs usually edging the page or type.

BOT Beginning of tape. Mark showing start point of computer tape.

bound books Term sometimes used for books where the coverboards are attached to the book before applying cover material or affixing endpapers. Much stronger than cased books and expensive to produce.

bourgeois Obsolete term for 9pt type.

bowl Typographical descriptive term for enclosed part of a letter as in a p or o. Also known as a **counter**.

boxed heading A ranged-left heading, as distinct from a **cross head** which is centred.

boxboard Card used in carton-making.

boxhead ruling Space at head of a ruled column where headings are to be inserted.

BPBIF British Paper and Board Industry Federation. The employers federation for paper merchants and mills in Britain.

bpi bits per inch The density at which data is encoded on a magnetic medium is expressed in bits per inch. 1600bpi is typical for standard magnetic tape.

BPIF British Printing Industries Federation. The employers federation representing the printing industry in Britain.

BPOP Bulk packed on pallets. Refers to consignments of sheets.

bpp Bits per pixel. Refers to the number of computer **bits** of information used by the computer to define each **pixel** or spot of information generated on a screen or on hard-copy (bromide, film). The number of bits used per pixel defines the number of **grey levels** that it is possible to display in each pixel. 1 bit per pixel means that only two 'grey' levels can be defined – 1 = white (on); or 0 = black (off). 2 bits per pixel mean that four grey levels can be defined: 11 binary (decimal number 3) = white; 10 binary (decimal 2) = light grey; binary 01 (decimal 1) = dark grey; and binary 00 (decimal 0) = black. And so on: 4 bits per pixel mean that 16 grey levels can be defined; and the best and most common for graphics arts, an 8 bits per pixel structure, means that 256 grey levels can be defined for each pixel (binary 11111111 = decimal 255 = complete white, down to binary 00000000 = decimal 0 = complete black). See also **colour monitor**.

bps Bits per second. See **baud**.

brace Form of bracket, mainly used in tables.

brackets Pairs of marks (), [], used in text. The round ones are also called **parentheses**. The square ones are known as **square brackets**.

BRAD Acronym for British Rate and Data. Publication listing all UK publications and their advertising specifications and requirements.

brass A die made from metal and used for **blocking**, eg, a **spine brass** which is used for blocking the spine of a case prior to casing in. A true 'brass' is made by engraving the metal, brass, mechanically. The normally used brass is produced photomechanically on copper, magnesium or zinc. See **chemac**, **zinco**.

brayer Small hand roller for applying ink when proofing.

breadboard A circuit board on which experimental circuits are assembled and tested.

break The interruption and control of transmission by the receiving device.

breaker In papermaking, the name of the machine which pre-dated the **hydrapulper** (q.v.). See **breaking**.

break for colour American term meaning to separate the components of a job into the individual formes necessary to print it in the colours needed.

breaking Term sometimes used to describe the mixing of pulps and their solution in water in the **hydrapulper** of a paper mill. The machines which pre-dated hydrapulpers were known as **breakers** or **breaking engines**.

breaking length Measurement of the limiting length of a uniformly wide strip of paper where the strip held by one end breaks due to its own weight.

breaking strength Paper measurement to determine comparative strengths.

break-line Term for the short last line of a paragraph. See also **club-line**,

paragraph widow.

break-up Pull apart a letterpress forme and distribute the type.

breve Short dish-shaped mark placed over a vowel to indicate it is short. The mark to indicate a long vowel is a straight line over the vowel called a **macron.**

brevier Obsolete type size, approximately 8 point.

brightness 1. Measure of a paper's reflectance of a standardised light. The result is expressed as an **ISO** factor. An 80gsm cartridge might be 85 ISO, for example. 2. Photographic term for the light reflected by the copy.

Brightype Obsolete machine which converted letterpress type and engravings to photographic images for use in offset lithography or gravure printing.

brilliant Obsolete term for 4pt type.

bristol Good quality **paperboard** with smooth finish.

British Standards Institution BSI British national co-ordinating body for technical standards in industry.

broadband transmission In communications, the ability to transmit along a frequency band which can be split into several narrower bands simultaneously so that different kinds of transmission - voice, video, data - can be transmitted at the same time. Contrast **narrowband transmission** (q.v.).

broadsheet Newspaper size approximating to A2 when folded.

broadside Traditional 'standard' sheet size from which the subdivisions of **quarto, sexto, octavo**, etc. derive.

brochure Promotional booklet about a company or product, often produced to a high quality to create an image of success.

broke Defective paper discarded during manufacture and usually repulped. Usually marked **xxx**. See also **retree.**

broken ream Part of a ream of paper left after use.

bromide Photographic light-sensitive paper used in photographic reproduction or phototypesetting, producing a positive image.

bronzing Process for obtaining a metallic printed effect. Metallic or bronze powder is applied to printed sizing ink while the ink is still wet giving a metallic lustre.

brownline See **brownprint**.

brown mechanical pulp Mechanical paper pulp produced from boiled or steamed wood.

brownprint Also known as a **Van Dyke** or **brownline**. Term (mainly used in America) for a photographic print from a negative used to check positioning before making printing plates. Similar to **blueprint** (q.v.).

brush coating Method of coating a web of paper where the coating mix is distributed by a set of stationary and oscillating brushes.

BS Number given to a British Standard published by the **British Standards Institution** (q.v.).

BSI British Standards Institution (q.v.).

BS 5750 British Standard for quality assurance and control in the printing industry.

bubble card See **blister pack**.

bubble cassette Removable and portable bubble memory available in cassettes of 64 and 256kb capacity.

bubble memory Form of backing storage which uses magnetically charged crystal chips to hold data. Not widely used.

bubble sort In which successive data items are exchanged if necessary starting with the first pair on a list.

buckle folder Machine for sheet folding where the sheet is bent or buckled by a metal plate. Also called a **plate folder**. The main alternative folding method is knife folding on a **knife folder** (q.v.).

buckram A heavy and strong binder's cloth made from woven textile stiffened with size.

buffer Computer storage used when information needs to be held temporarily en route from one device to another.

buffered carton Heavy-duty mailing carton with protruding buffers at either end to absorb accidental impact.

bug Computer term for a programming defect which interferes with a computer operation.

built-up letter Graphic term for a letter which is first drawn and filled in

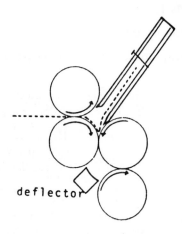

Illus 10. Principle of buckle folding.

afterwards.

bulk Paper term used to describe the degree of thickness of paper. Measured by **caliper, volume** or **ppi** pages per inch (American).

bulk basis Obsolete paper term describing the thickness (32nds of an inch) of 320 pages in 60lb quad crown (68gsm).

bulk between boards The total thickness of a **book block** (q.v.) without counting the thickness of the front and back boards.

bulking dummy A blank book to show the paper being proposed and the bulk that this paper will achieve.

bulking index American paper measurement of bulk formed by dividing the thickness of a sheet (in inches) by its basis weight, or the inches of thickness per pound of basis weight.

bulking number American paper measurement of the number of sheets that bulk to 1 inch in thickness under standard pressure. Multiply bulking number by 2 to give pages per inch **(ppi)**.

bulk wrapping Wrapping several copies of a periodical, as distinct from individual wrapping.

bulky mechanical Also **bulky news**. Grades of paper made predominantly from mechanical pulp to a specific and high bulk, e.g. as often used for cheap paper-back books.

bulldog First edition of a daily paper.

bullet Phototypesetting term for a large dot used for ornamentation.

bulletin News sheet.

bulls eye See **hickey**.

bump exposure Photographic term describing method of increasing highlight contrast when producing a half-tone by removing the screen briefly to remove any dots in the highlight area.

bumping blocks Use of delicate hammering from the back of a letterpress block to raise the height of various parts.

bundling Compressing the folded sections at the beginning of the binding process in a special bundling press which squashes the sections flat and expels the air from them prior to further processing.

burin A pointed engraver's steel tool used for cutting.

burn Platemaking term for an exposure.

burn out mask An opaque mask used in platemaking to protect the image areas of a printing plate while the non-image areas are exposed for long enough to burn out all remaining unwanted traces of sellotape, edge marks etc. Used on **positive-working plates**.

burr A rough edge of metal left after burnishing or cutting.

burst Rupture of a paper web due to one of a variety of causes, e.g. the reel being too tightly wound or air trapped into the reel when winding.

burst binding A form of unsewn adhesive binding where the sections are 'burst' or punched along the spines, typically on a web printing press, thus giving extra adhesion between sheets as well as sections when the sections are bound. Also known as **punch binding**. See also **notch binding**.

burst factor A measure of the **bursting strength** of a paper (q.v.).

burst index A measurement of paper bursting strength relative to grammage under standard test conditions.

bursting strength The strength of a paper to resist a uniformly distributed pressure under test conditions.

bus In computer architecture, an internal path by which signals travel to an from various components in the system. The signals may be of a particular kind, such as 'data bus' or 'address bus'.

business press Periodicals directed to the business and professional sectors.

butted lines Linecast slugs placed side by side producing a single line of type.

butterfly wings See **wing effect**.

B/W Black and white.

byline Writer's or journalist's name on an article or newspaper story.

byte The smallest addressable unit of storage in computer memory, usually eight bits in length. See **bit, kilobyte, megabyte, gigabyte**.

C

C 1. A high-level programming language developed for the UNIX operating system on Digital Equipment Corporation PDP 11/70 minicomputers. 2. The **C series** is an international **ISO** range of sizes for envelopes, designed to accommodate stationery in the **A series** sizes (q.v.).

C1S Paper coated on one side.

C2S Paper coated on both sides.

CAD cash against documents A payment arrangement that allows for the goods with their documents to be sent to the care of a specified bank, who will release the goods only in exchange for the payment due.

CAD/CAM Computer Aided Design/Computer Aided Manufacture. A number of CAD/CAM techniques have found their way through into the graphics arts area, notably in mask-cutting for colour planning.

CAF Currency Adjustment Factor. In seafreight, an adjustment to scale charges made to recover or pass on the effects of exchange rate fluctuations.

calcium carbonate Chalk pigment used as a filler in some papers and as a white coating mix. It is an alkaline substance, and as a filler it is associated particularly with **acid-free** papers. There are two basic kinds used in papermaking: pcc and gcc. The first, **pcc**, precipitated calcium carbonate, is the finer and better sort; the second, **gcc**, ground calcium carbonate, is rather more coarse.

calcium hypochlorite Used for bleaching paper.

calendered Describes paper which has been given a smooth finish by passing it through a **calender stack** (q.v.).

calender section The final part of a Fourdrinier paper machine which contains the **calender stack** (q.v.).

calender stack A set of rollers on a paper machine which give a smooth finish to the web as it passes through by applying pressure. Calendered paper has a smooth, medium gloss finish. See also **supercalender**.

calf Leather of high quality used in bookbinding.

calf cloth An imitation leather binding material.

california case A kind of type case which accommodates both upper and lower case letters.

caliper The thickness of a sheet of paper or board, measured with a micrometer and usually expressed in thousandths-of-a-millimetre (microns).

caliper shear burst Web break during winding caused by variations in roller nip.

calligraphy The art of handwriting or script drawing. Traditionally, calligraphic letterforms have a strong 45 degree 'stress' (pen pressure) which results in letter strokes which contrast strongly with each other. Letter strokes which form at 45 degrees downwards (backslashes) are thick, reflecting the pressure of the pen at this angle; letter strokes which form at 45 degrees upwards (forward slashes) are thin. Vertical strokes are commonly thin.

camber Convex surface of a roll of paper.

cambric One of several finishes typically available in imitation cloths. Cambric is a delicate fine-linen finish.

Cambridge Ring A **LAN**, **local area network**, which unlike the **Ethernet** configuration (q.v.), is circular. A series of **repeaters** strengthen the signals as they are sent round the ring, and simultaneously check for and report on errors.

cameo Relief die stamping process.

camera ready artwork or **camera ready copy** (**CRC**) or **camera ready paste-up** (**CRPU**) Type-matter or type and line artwork pasted up into position ready for photographing.

Cameron belt press A web book press which, linked to a binding line, can print, gather and bind a substantial book in one pass. Used primarily for paperbacks.

cancel 1. To remove a leaf in a book and replace it with another. 2. A reprinted single leaf or set of pages for replacing a number of pages in a book which have to be suppressed (normally because of a major error or libel problems).

c&sc Capitals and small capitals, i.e. words which begin with capitals and have the other characters in small caps the height of the lower case body size.

THIS IS AN EXAMPLE OF CAPS AND SMALL CAPS.

Illus 11. Capitals and small capitals.

canon Obsolete term for 48 point type.

canvas Bookbinding cloth of good strength. Also known as **art canvas** (q.v.).

canvas note A type of embossed stationery which simulates canvas.

capacitor A device that introduces a capacitance to an electric circuit.

cap height The height of the capital letters of a fount.

capillary rise The distance liquid travels vertically up a strip of paper, measured by standard test.

caps Capitals. Upper case letters, e.g. A, B, C, etc. See also **lower case**.

caption Text accompanying and describing an illustration.

carbon black Intensely black pigment used in ink manufacture.

carbon paper Lightweight paper coated on one side with transferable colouring agent for producing copies by impression on to an underlying sheet. **One-time carbon** is used when disposable carbon sheets are convenient.

carbro Continuous tone colour print.

carbro process Photographic technique for correcting colour before the positive stage.

card See **board**.

cardboard Any stiff sheet of card, usually comprising several layers of paper pasted together.

card chase Small **chase** (q.v.) used for small stationery composition.

carding Thin spacing of lines of type.

card punch Keyboard machine which perforates cards for data storage or input. A **card reader** reads the data.

card reader A device that produces signals from holes sensed in a punched card.

caret Proof reader's mark indicating an insertion.

carriage paid Refers to a deal where goods are delivered with the freight element paid by the sender. See also **cif**.

carriage return Keyboard command key which terminates a line of setting and may enter text from a computer screen into memory.

carrier sheet Sheet of paper inside film wrapping which carries the address label.

carton Cardboard box for packing.

cartridge Printing or drawing paper with good dimensional stability, high opacity and good bulk. Often used in bookwork.

cartridge disc Computer storage disc enclosed in a plastic case.

case 1. Stiff board cover of a book often covered with cloth, paper or leather which is attached to the **book-block** (q.v.) hence **case-bound**. **Casing-in** is the process of attaching the case to the book-block, often performed by a **casing-in machine**. 2. Partitioned tray containing type for hand composition. See also **lower case** and **upper case**.

case board Board used for casemaking, typically **Dutch grey board** or **unlined chipboard**. Typical caliper/gsm ranges are from 1725 microns/1120gsm at the lower end up to 3000 microns/1750gsm.

case-bound Referring to a book with a hard case. Also **cased, hardback**. See also **limp-bound**.

cased binding Binding with a hard case as opposed to **paperback binding** with a paper cover.

case material The material, or **imitation cloth**, which covers the case boards to form the case of a hardback book.

cassette 1. Light-proof container for photographic film or roll paper. 2. Small reel-to-reel tape holder for audio or data recording. In storage terms, a C10 (ten-minute) tape will hold around 60K (20 A4's of text); or in other words, 6K per minute of running time (around 2 A4's of text).

cassie Damaged paper at the top and bottom of a ream.

cast coated Paper given a high gloss by pressure from a polished, heated cylinder before the coating dries.

casting 1. The process of forcing molten metal into a mould to create a character or slug of type. 2. Producing **stereotypes** (q.v.) in newspaper printing. A **casting box** is used for this purpose.

casting off Calculating the number of pages a given amount of copy will make when set in a given type-face and size to a given area.

catalogue Book or booklet which presents details of goods or services, often including prices and ordering routines.

Cataloguing in Publication data A system operated by the British Library offering classified entries which publishers can print on the imprint pages of their books to facilitate library cataloguing, bibliographical compilation, etc. The equivalent in the USA is the **Library of Congress (Lib Con) number** (q.v.).

> British Library Cataloguing in Publication Data
> Faux, Ian
>   Litho printing. —— New ed., rev. and
>   updated. —— (Publisher's guide series).
>   1. Offset printing
>   I. Title   II. Faux, Ian, Printing by
>   lithography   II. Series
>   686.2'315   Z252.5.L5
>
>   ISBN 0-948905-03-4

Illus 12. Example of British Library Cataloguing in Publication data.

catch line A temporary heading on a manuscript or proof for identification.

catch-stitch See **kettle-stitch**.

catch-up Scumming (q.v.) on a litho printing plate.

cathode The negative terminal of an electronic component. The **anode** is the positive terminal.

cathode ray tube, CRT Display screen activated by an electron **gun** (q.v.). Also known as a **monitor**. In the case of a monochrome monitor, there is a single gun. In the case of a colour monitor, there are three guns responding individually to red (R), green (G), and blue (B) signals, and which beamed together are capable of many millions of shades. See also **bpp** (bits per pixel), **colour monitor**.

cc Copies (plural).

CCD Charge Coupled Device. The reading device in most scanners: a photodiode which reacts to areas of dark and light and generates a different voltage signal for each separate shade or **grey level** it detects. Each separate voltage is then translated into binary data.

CCI 1. **Computer-controlled inking** (q.v.). 2. The name of the computer-controlled inking system used with MAN Roland printing machines.

CCITT The International Telephone and Telegraph Consultative Committee. The CCITT is an advisory committee established under the United Nations to recommend worldwide standards in the field of public telecommunication services.

CCR Complementary colour removal. See **achromatic separation.**

CD 1. **Compact disc:** a variety of **optical disc** made in a standard small format (4.72" diameter) and carrying digital information. A **CD-ROM** (compact disc, read-only memory) is essentially a text and graphics storage medium, typically running an indexed database. Although the total digital capacity of a standard CD-ROM is around 600 Mb, the indexing functions require a considerable amount of room, and typically around 350 Mb is available for database text (somewhere over 50 million words of text). 2. In papermaking, **cross direction** (q.v.), as distinct from **MD, machine direction.**

C-DOS Concurrent DOS: a version of **DOS** developed by Digital Research for the higher grades of IBM PC (AT and compatibles) which permits **multi-tasking** and multi-user operation.

cell Storage area for a single unit of information. An element of a spreadsheet into which data formulae may be stored.

celluloid proof Proof on transparent sheet, one per colour printed, used for checking register. See also **plastic proof.**

cellulose Complex fibrous substance forming the walls of plant cells, and the prime raw material in **pulp. Cellulose acetate** is used in making film.

central processing unit See **CPU.**

centre To position type centrally in a given measure.

centred point A raised dot, centred on the x-height of the fount, used as a decimal point (rather than one aligned on the base line of the fount).

centre-feed Paper tape sprocket holes that line up with the middle of code holes. See also **advance feed.**

centre notes Notes placed between columns of a page.

centre spread The two facing pages at the centre of a **signature** (q.v.).

centrifugal cleaner Device which removes unwanted material from paper fibres by centrifugal force.

Centronics interface A parallel interface standard for data transmission commonly used between microcomputers and printers and consisting of eight parallel lines. See **parallel transmission**.

certificate of origin A certificate stating details of where a commodity has been manufactured.

chad The waste punched out of paper tape or cards.

CGA Colour graphics adapter: IBM PC standard to drive a colour monitor.

chain lines The wider watermark lines which run at right angles to the narrow **laid lines** on **laid papers** (q.v.).

chalk See **calcium carbonate**.

chalking Powdering of ink which has not adhered properly to paper.

chalk overlay Letterpress overlay for indicating adjustment to printing pressure.

channel 1. In communications, an electrical path along which signals can be sent. Digital leased-lines, such as a **kilostream link**, can be split via a **multiplexor** device into a number of different channels supporting (for example) voice, fax and data simultaneously. 2. Row of holes in punched tape.

chapel Smallest unit of a print union's departmental or company grouping. **Father of chapel** (FOC) or **Mother of chapel** is the elected chairperson.

chapter drop White space between the head of the chapter title and the head of the type area of a book.

chapter head Chapter title and/or number.

character Letter, figure or symbol of type. See also **en, keystroke.**

character code Numeric representation of a character. See, for example, **ASCII**.

character compensation Global reduction or expansion in character fit by adjustment to the normal set width values resident in a typesetting system's computer. Also called **track kerning** or **tracking**.

character count Total number of characters and spaces in a piece of copy.

character fit Space between letters which can be reduced or expanded.

character generation Projection of type images on a cathode ray tube.

character printer A printer which prints individual characters as distinct from complete lines. Often capable of reproducing specific typefaces.

character reader Alternative term for an **OCR** reading device.

character recognition Scanning characters by machine, often for digital storage. Also, **optical character recognition, OCR**.

character set The full range of characters on a keyboard in memory or available for output from a machine.

characters per second cps A measure of data transmission rate. See also **baud**.

character subset Any group of characters taken from a character set which have a common feature. See **character set**.

charge coupled device See **CCD**.

Chartpak Rub-down rules of varying thicknesses provided on rolls for applying frames or lines to camera-ready artwork.

chase Rectangular steel frame in which type and blocks are locked up for letterpress printing.

chassis The metal base or structure on to which the electronic components of a computer are assembled.

check bit A binary digit (or digits) employed as a check for the presence of errors in a related set of digits.

check digit An extra digit calculated automatically from other digits in a data item and used to check its accuracy.

check disc A command common to several operating systems and used to check the index and file space allocation of a disc and return a status report.

chemac A copper die used for blocking. Made by photochemical methods, unlike a true brass which is engraved on brass by hand.

chemical ghosting Ghost images on sheets caused by the chemical reaction of inks.

chemical pulp Pulp obtained from wood or other plant sources by chemical removal of impurities rather than mechanical processing.

chemical transfer Process of transferring an image from one surface to another under pressure and chemical reaction. Used for certain kinds of small-offset printing plate. Abbreviated **CT**.

chemi-thermomechanical pulp CTMP Thermomechanical pulp (q.v.) which undergoes further chemical treatment resulting in a pulp not far below the quality of **woodfree** pulp. The very best quality of **mechanical pulp** made.

cheque paper Special paper used for cheques and having a surface which betrays attempts at alteration.

Cheshire Proprietary name of machine which sticks labels to envelopes or wrappers.

chill roll Cooled roller, used for setting ink after drying in a web-offset machine.

china clay White clay used for loading and coating paper.

Chinese white Paint used in re-touching artwork.

chip or **microchip** 1. A small electronic component containing extensive logic circuits. Two of the leading chip manufacturers whose products are used extensively in microcomputers are Intel and Motorola. Intel supplies the processors used in IBM micros, and in advancing order of power they are the 8086, the 8088 (used in the IBM XT), the 80286 (used in the IBM AT), the 80386 and the 80486. Motorola manufacture the chips for Apple and many others; their main chips are the 68000 (AppleMac Plus, AppleMac SE, AppleMac Portable); the 68020 (AppleMac II); and the 68030 (AppleMac IIx, AppleMac IIcx, AppleMac IIci). 2. Woodchip used in pulpmaking. 3. Trim (US).

chipboard See **unlined chipboard**.

chipper A machine which chips logs after debarking.

choke In colour film masking and assembly, the fractional overlapping or obtrusion of an image area which fits around a reversed-out area into the boundary of the latter, so that a fit with no white fringes is ensured. Compare **overdraw**, in which the reversed-out image is the one made fractionally larger so that it obtrudes into the outer image area.

chlorine dioxide A gas used in the **bleaching** processes of chemical pulp.

chroma Purity of colour.

chromatic aberration The inability of a lens to bring light of all colours to a common point of focus. See also **apochromatic**.

chromolithograph or **chromo** Colour print made by a form of lithographic printing used in the late nineteenth century and conspicuous by its vivid and lasting colours.

cicero European 12pt unit of type measure. Equal to 4.511mm.

CIELab Scales of colour measurement used by the International Commission on Illumination.

CIF Cost, insurance and freight. A price quoted cif includes all charges up to delivery at the quayside at the port of destination. Contrast **FOB**.

CIP data See **Cataloguing in Publication data**.

circuit board See **printed circuit board**.

circular Printed leaflet distributed to prospective purchasers.

circular screen Half-tone screen which can be rotated to obtain proper screen angles for colour half-tones.

circulating matrix The Linotype matrix from which type is cast.

circulation Total copies of a publication distributed.

circumferential movement Adjustment of a plate in press makeready around the circumference of the plate cylinder rather than from side to side (**lateral movement**).

clamshell A type of small platen printing machine.

clasp envelope Envelope held closed by a metal clasp.

classified Advertisements for job vacancies, articles for sale, etc, set in columns and sorted by classification.

clay See **china clay**.

clean Correct a proof, or a list of names and addresses, etc.

clean line An electrical power line dedicated to one machine and therefore not subject to **spiking** (q.v.).

clean proof A printer's proof in which there are no errors.

clean tape Computer tape with no data on it or with all unnecessary codes removed.

clearance agent A freight-forwarder responsible for clearing consignments through customs.

Clear To Send (CTS) A signal sent by a receiving device in answer to a **Request To Send (RTS)** signal. See **handshake**.

cleat binding A method of binding single leaves using a form of **side-sewing** (q.v.).

clip art Standard drawn images available for stock illustration and offered by a number of graphics software packages.

clipboard In DTP page make-up, that area of the screen outside the defined page grids which can be used for storing set text, illustrations, etc, prior to placing within the page boundaries using the 'paste' command.

clipping area The area defined within a **clipping boundary** (q.v.).

clipping boundary The outline boundary around an image which defines its shape and excludes other images from intruding into it.

clipping path The direction or set of directions which make up a **clipping boundary** (q.v.).

clock The synchronising element of a computer. A register whose contents change at regular intervals in order to establish a time constant.

clock speed The operating speed of a computer, measured in **megahertz, MHz** (q.v.).

clone In computing, a machine which closely resembles a leading computer product and is compatible with it in all major respects, but normally aims to undercut it on price (eg, the wide range of IBM micro clones).

closed loop A sequence of computer instructions repeated indefinitely. While closed looping can be introduced deliberately, the phenomenon can also result from a programming fault.

close up Reduce spacing between characters of type or other elements on a proof.

closing date See **copy date**.

cloth binding The use of cloth to cover the boards of a case-bound book.

cloth centred paper Paper with a linen centre, often used for maps when much re-folding is anticipated.

clothings Pieces of leather or cloth fixed at the backs of stationery books for strengthening.

cloth joint A strip of cloth which strengthens the joints of a bound book (usually attached to the endpapers).

cloth lined paper Paper backed with linen or muslin for additional strength.

club line Strictly, the short last line of a paragraph at the bottom of a page. But also used frequently as a synonym for **orphan** (q.v.) too, and therefore by extension to mean any short line at the foot of a page.

cluster In computing, a sequence of **tracks** which together hold the data in a file.

CMOS Complementary metal-oxide semiconductor. In computer hardware, an advanced form of **semiconductor** bearing an integrated logic system and requiring very little electrical power. Used in the **ROM** circuitry of a number of microcomputers.

CMYK Abbreviation for cyan, magenta, yellow, key (black) – the four process colours.

coated cartridge Dull-finish coated paper, normally **blade-coated**, very commonly used for printing colour books.

coated paper Paper coated with china clay or similar to give a smooth surface suitable for half-tone reproduction. **Coating slip** is the coating mixture. **Coating binder** is the part of the coating mixture which ensures adhesion to the body stock. **Coat weight** is the amount of coating on the base paper, expressed as dry weight on a given area, ie. in gsm.

coating 1. Light sensitive surface applied to litho plate. 2. Clear protective varnish applied to printed surface for protection. 3. China clay mixture used on paper. See **coated paper**.

coating binder That part of a coating formulation whose purpose is to bind the pigment system to the body stock and to obtain many of the desired properties of the final coated paper, such as pick and water resistance, ink receptivity, flexibility, gloss and blister resistance. Binders are obtained from natural sources like starch, casein and soya protein or can be produced synthetically.

coating mix or **coat mix** or **coating slip** White suspension of china clay or calcium carbonate and other pigments, which is applied to base paper by blade or roller and which when dry forms the matt or gloss coat.

coat weight The amount of coating on a base paper expressed as dry weight on a given area, ie. gsm.

Cobb size test A measurement of the **sizing** of paper by water absorbed under specified conditions.

COBOL Common Business-Oriented Language. High-level computer programming language widely used in commercial data processing.

cocked-up initial Initial letter in a new line which is larger than the characters in the rest of the line, but which sits on the same baseline as them. Compare **drop initial**.

This is a cocked-up initial.

Illus 13. A cocked-up initial.

cockle Puckered finish to a sheet of paper created during the drying process to add crispness.

cockling Wavy edges on paper caused by unstable atmospheric conditions.

COD Cash On Delivery. Method of despatch which requires the recipient to pay on receipt of goods.

code A character string or line of symbolic instructions to a computer.

code conversion The process of altering the numeric representation of one group of characters to that required by a different system, language or process.

code set Coding system, or systematic set of codes. **ASCII**, **EBCDIC**, or **TTS**, for example, are typical code sets. See also **transmission codes**.

co-edition Edition of a book whose cost of production (and sometimes editorial development) is shared between a number of partners, typically in different countries and with different marketing territories and interests.

cold colour Colour containing blue tones.

cold composition Any typesetting method which does not use hot metal for casting.

cold-melt An adhesive such as **PVA** (q.v.) which is applied for binding purposes at room temperature. Contrast **hot-melt**.

cold-set Web printing in which the ink is allowed to dry by penetration on an absorbent paper without heat. See also **heat-set**.

cold start The act of starting a computer after the power supply has been switched off before. At this stage the device has no operating programs in memory and these have to be loaded from **backing store** or from **ROM**. Compare **warm start**.

collage Image comprised of a number of items collected together as a visual whole.

collate Loosely used to mean **'gather'** (q.v.); but strictly, to check the gathered sections to establish that they are in the correct sequence. **Collating marks** on the back folds assist in this.

collating marks Black marks on the back folds of sections in sequential positions used for checking that the sections are in the correct order after gathering.

college electro A plastic-backed electrotype invented at the London College of Printing.

collotype A short-run, screenless printing process using gelatine coated plates to produce continuous tone reproduction.

colophon A printer's or publisher's identifying emblem or symbol, printed on spines and title pages. Compare **logotype.**

colour bars Coloured strips on four-colour process proofs showing densities across a sheet and revealing other printing characteristics.

colour blanks Printed sheets with illustrations only but no text. Produced in this way typically in expectation of language changes for co-editions, etc.

colour breaks The separate colour overlays for each overlay in a four colour set (US).

colour cast An excess of one shade or hue in a subject for reproduction or in a printed subject.

colour comp print Paper print made from a transparency.

colour correction Changing colour values in a set of separations by dot-etching, masking or retouching.

coloured edges Dyed edges on a book block.

coloured tops Dyed tops on a book block.

colour etching The process of altering dot sizes on a four-colour separation film by local retouching in order to strengthen or weaken a particular colour in a particular area and so affect the printed result.

colour fall In multi-unit web-offset printing, the sequences of pages on which colour will be available as dictated by the press configuration used.

colour filters Sheets which are placed in front of a camera lens to filter out all colours except that selected, thereby producing separated films for four-colour process work.

colour guide Instructions on artwork indicating colour requirements.

colour line separation artwork Artwork supplied already separated into its component printing colours with one registered overlay per colour.

colour-matching system Method of colour specification by matching the colour required to one in a swatch of colours provided as a set. Each colour in the swatch has its ink-mix formula described. An example is the Pantone matching system (PMS).

colour monitor A CRT screen which displays full colour. Top-level colour monitors can address and display 16.7 million possible colours (256 possible values for each pixel displayed by the red (R) gun, multiplied by 256 possible values from the green (G) gun, multiplied by 256 possible values from the blue (B) gun). These systems are sometimes known as 24-bit colour systems (8 bits per pixel for each colour, and 3 colours). See also **bpp (bits per pixel)**, **CRT**, **RGB**.

colour overleaf proofs See **acetate proofs**.

colour proofs Proofs in the final colours required, produced either by a plastic laminate proofing method (**Cromalin** or similar) or by printing from plates (**machine proofing** or **wet proofing**).

colour separation Separating full colour into the four process colours by means of scanning or of filters, resulting in four films used to make printing plates.

colour separation negative One negative out of a set of four separated process colour negatives.

colour sequence The order in which the four process colours are printed.

colour splits Instructions for the allocation of correct printing colours to individual components of a piece of integral artwork.

colour swatch A sample of a specified colour.

colour transparency A full colour photographic positive on film.

column 1. Vertical area of print comprising lines of the same measure. 2. Regular newspaper article.

column balancing In desktop publishing, the automatic adjustment of columns to create a visual evenness.

column centimetre See **column inch**.

column inch A newspaper measure of text space: one column wide and one inch deep.

column rule Light vertical rule used to separate text which runs in columns.

COM A filename extension common to several operating systems and identifying a system command file – namely, one that can be run by typing the first portion of the filename. For example, DBASE.COM would be loaded and run by typing DBASE.

combination folder A machine combining a buckle and knife folder.

combination line and tone A single print or piece of film combining half-tone and line work.

comic strip Cartoon drawings in sequence, appearing regularly in a periodical.

coming and going A head-to-head imposition mostly associated with massmarket paperbacks in which two copies of a book result from one set of plates. The first page of the book is imposed head-to-head with the last page, and soon on until the middle is reached. After printing and binding the two copies of the book are separated.

command A computer instruction issued from the keyboard and specifying an operation.

command processor One of the fundamental parts of a computer's operating system, this is the program which loads, validates, and then executes commands issued from the keyboard of the computer. In the operating system for IBM micros **DOS**, the file is named 'command.com'. In UNIX it is called the **shell**.

commercial invoice An invoice against which payment is to be made. Compare **pro-forma invoice**.

commercial register Colour printing to a register tolerance of plus or minus one row of dots.

common The cash column on ruled stationery.

common-impression press Design of printing press in which two sets of plate/blanket cylinders mounted opposite each other use one common impression cylinder. In the case of four- or six-colour machines, second or third 'tandem' units follow on from the first tandem unit in the same way, each unit printing two colours. Also known as the **five-cylinder layout press,** and the **tandem press.** Contrast the design of the **unit press** (q.v.).

communication The electronic transfer of data between different hardware. Also known as **comms.**

comp 1. To **compose** (q.v.). 2. A **compositor** (q.v.). 3. A **comprehensive** (US): a layout showing everything in position. 4. Complimentary subscription to or copy of a periodical.

compact disc See **CD-ROM.**

compatibility The ability of two pieces of electronic hardware to work in conjunction and to communicate with each other.

compiler A computer program which checks and converts programs from a **high-level language** into **machine-code.** The resulting machine-code program then becomes the program accessed by the computer, resulting in faster processing speeds. Compare **interpreter**, which is a program sometimes in **ROM** that takes a high-level language program one line at a time and changes it into machine-code instructions every time the program is run. See also **assembler**, which is a program which changes a **low-level language** into machine code.

complementary colour removal See **achromatic separations.**.

compliance In computing, compliance to a standard indicates adherence in all respects to the requirements of that standard.

complimentary copy Copy of a book given free.

comp list List of periodical subscribers receiving complimentary copies.

component stress Pertaining to factors of usage such as shock, temperature, voltage level, etc. which may affect the efficiency of a component.

compose To make up type into lines and/or pages. The operator is called a **compositor.**

composing stick A hand-held, adjustable tray in which a compositor sets type by hand.

composite block A plate comprising more than one original.

composite page negatives (positives) Negatives or positives made up from several different pieces taped or cemented together, as opposed to final **one-piece** negatives or positives.

composition sizes Types under 14pt in size. As distinct from **display sizes** (q.v.).

This is 6pt type.

This is 8pt type.

This is 9pt type.

This is 10pt type.

This is 12pt type.

Illus 14. Composition sizes of type.

compositor Typesetter who makes up pages.

comprehensive (US) A **visual,** or layout showing everything in position. Also, **comp.**

computer-aided design See **CAD.**

computer-assisted learning In which a computer is used to raise questions and assess a student's response.

computer-controlled inking CCI The use of equipment which sets and monitors correct ink-flows on the press and makes automatic adjustments for make-ready and during running.

computer typesetting The use of a computer to store and display typesetting and to perform many other functions such as hyphenation and justification.

computer word Any group of characters that are capable of being treated as a single unit for the purposes of processing or storage. Common computer-word lengths are 8-bit, 16-bit and 32-bit.

concurrent processing The execution of two programs simultaneously.

condensed type A typeface with narrow characteristics.

conditioning The deliberate exposure of paper to local atmospheric conditions so that its moisture content matches the ambient atmosphere. Optimum press room conditions for printing are around 20⁰c, 55-65RH; and under these conditions the moisture content of the paper to be printed should be 7-8%. Drier than this, might cause **tight edges** in the stack; damper than this, **wavy edges** (q.v.). Both conditions can lead to creasing on the press, or difficulties with register.

cone refiner In papermaking, the cone-shaped piece of machinery into which the stock is pumped from the **hydrapulper** in order to undergo further beating or **refining**. After this stage, the stock is cleaned in a series of **centrifugal cleaners** and finally pumped to the **headbox** for the beginning of the Fourdrinier process.

configuration The arrangement of peripherals into a computer system.

confirmed irrevocable letter of credit See **letter of credit**.

conformability The degree in which a paper surface will change shape to contact ink on the press.

connected dot Half-tone dots joined together.

console The keyboard which controls the operations of a mainframe computer.

constat Short for **continuous stationery**.

consumable textbook A book which can be written in by the student and therefore can be used only once.

consumer press Periodicals circulating widely among the general public (as distinct from trade and technical press).

contact print A photographic print of a negative or positive made in contact with, and therefore the same size as, the original.

contact screen Half-tone screen used in direct contact with the photographic film for creating half-tones.

container Standard sized metal box used for cargo in sea and land freight. Containers come in two standard sizes: the first 20' x 8' x $8^1/_2$' (6096 x 2438 x 2588mm), the second double this 40' x 8' x $8^1/_2$' (12192 x 2438 x 2588mm). A 20 foot container will typically take 24 **pallet**-loads (6 pallets lengthwise x 2 pallets widthwise x 2 layers); and a 40 foot container will take double this amount. Typical 20' container loads might be 30,000 books of average 8vo size (around 12/15 tonnes).

container boards Boards used in manufacturing box containers.

contents page Page of a book or magazine explaining the contents and where they appear.

continuous pulping Pulp produced in a constantly running digester.

continuous stationery Reel stationery used on computer printers and other automatic machines.

continuous tone Unscreened films containing genuine grey levels.

contone See **continuous tone**.

contraries Unwanted material in paper or stock.

contrast Wide range of tonal gradations.

contrast ratio opacity Paper opacity measured by the **TAPPI** method of gauging reflectance from a backed sheet.

control bus That part of a computer's internal circuitry which transports signals designed to control system operations.

control codes Embedded codes in a file used to drive a peripheral, usually a printer.

controlled circulation Magazine or newspaper distribution free to selected names or groups of readers.

control tape Computer tape containing control information rather than data.

control unit Part of a computer **CPU** which sequences operations.

conversion systems Systems which convert type or plates into film for subsequent printing by a different method.

converter A computer peripheral which transfers data from one medium to another.

converter press Also **convertible press**. A press that will print either one-colour on each side of the sheet in one pass, or two-colour on one side of the sheet in one pass.

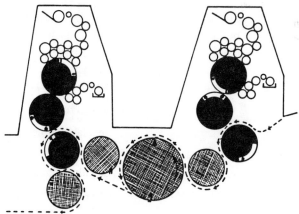

Illus 15. A Heidelberg GTO convertible press.

converting Sheeting, re-reeling or otherwise changing the format of sheets or reels of paper. The person who carries this out is known as a **converter**.

cooking Treating **pulp** with heat, water and chemicals.

copier paper Paper used in photocopying machines.

copperprint The developed image on a plate before etching.

co-processor In computing, an extra processor inserted to work alongside the main **CPU** and assist it in performing special tasks (maths, etc).

copy Material for publication, especially manuscript for typesetting.

copy block Block of typesetting treated as a unit.

copyboard Holding frame for material being photographed for reproduction.

copy date Scheduled date for delivering copy to a publisher or printer.

copyfitting Determining the typographical specification to which a manuscript needs to be set in order to fill a given amount of space.

copyholder 1. Piece of equipment which holds manuscript copy upwards for easy reading by the keyboard operator. 2. Proof reader who reads aloud to a colleague who checks text.

copy prep Copy preparation. Putting instructions on a manuscript to ensure understanding of the requirement by the compositor. See also **electronic mark-up**.

copyright The sole right to reproduce a work in any material form or to publish it. A normal copyright term is 50 years from the date of publication.

copyright page Title page verso of a book containing bibliographic information. Also known as the **biblio page**.

CORA V Linotype's typesetter-command language for the Linotron 202 and other machines.

cording Putting cord into stationery as a form of loose binding.

core memory Main storage capacity in the central processing unit of a computer. Defined in thousands or millions of **bytes**, indicated by the term K or M.

corrigenda List of corrections printed in a book. Contrast **erratum slip**

which is a separate insert or tipped-in list of errors.

corrs Corrections.

corrugated Packaging grade of cardboard made by sandwiching fluted kraft paper between sheets of cardboard to absorb any impact.

corruption An unwanted alteration of data during transmission or while held on a backing medium.

cotton content paper See **rag paper**.

cotton linters Cotton seed-hair fibres used in fine paper.

couch End of the wet end of a paper machine where the web is passed to the press section.

counter Centre part of a letter enclosed by strokes, such as the bowl of an O. Also, **bowl**.

counterpack Point-of-sale display box holding a small number of featured books.

counting keyboard Keyboard which has logic for justification purposes.

cover Outer section of a periodical, bearing its title.

cover boards Lightweight boards, normally in the range 200-300gsm, for the covers of paperback or limpbound books.

covering 1. See **case material**. Non-woven materials, woven materials and leathers comprise the most commonly used coverings. 2. The fixing of a book cover to the spine and endpapers.

covering power The opacity achieved by a printing ink.

CPC Computer Print Control A computer-controlled makeready and inking system used with Heidelberg printing machines. See also **CCI**.

cpi Characters per inch. Unit of measurement of type in a line.

cpm Copies per minute. A measurement commonly quoted to describe the speed at which laser printers output sheets. It is a potentially misleading description, because it is used to indicate the mechanical speed at which the printer engine produces not the first but the subsequent copies once the data for the first copy is 'composed' inside the printer's memory; depending on the complexity of the document the first copy may take up to five times as long to produce as subsequent copies from the same original. A standard figure might be 8-10 copies per minute. Also, **ppm**, **pages per minute**.

CP/M Control Program for Microcomputers. An early single-user operating system developed by Digital Research.

cpp Characters per pica. Copyfitting method using average number of characters per **pica** (q.v.).

C print See **C type**.

cps Characters per second: a measurement of the output speed of a phototypesetter or printer. cps x 10 = approximate words per minute (**wpm**).

CPU Central processing unit: the computing unit in an electronic system. It consists of a control unit (**CU**) which interpets external commands and issues instructions inside the computer for their execution; an arithmetic and logic unit (**ALU**) which performs arithmetic and logic operations on data provided; and main memory (**RAM** and **ROM**) which holds the data to be manipulated and the instructions issued, and stores the results of processing. In a micro, the CPU is termed a **microprocessor** and typically consists of a single **LSI chip**.

cracked edge Broken edge on a web of paper.

crash 1. Serious hardware or software failure in a computer system. 2. Muslin cloth or **mull** as a **first lining** on the spines of the sections in a cased-bound book.

crash finish Linen-look finish on imitation cloth.

crawling Contraction of ink on paper when it has not penetrated the surface.

CRC See **camera ready copy**.

crease 1. Impress an indented line across a sheet of paper or board to assist folding. 2. A folding fault which leaves a crease in the sheet, hence **creasing**.

creep 1. Blanket movement during printing. 2. The effect of the back margins of the outer pages in a printed section becoming narrower than the back margins of the inner pages, due to the thickness of paper across the fold. Needs to be compensated for in imposition by **shingling** (q.v.).

creping Crinkling paper to create a soft, elastic sheet.

critical path The sequence of events which takes the shortest time. Analysis of the critical path ensures that events on the path are never delayed, while events on less critical paths may be if necessary.

crocking Dry ink rubbed off after printing.

Cromalin A proprietary plastic-proofing system for proofing four-colour subjects without making machine plates. See **plastic proof.**

crop Cut back part of an illustration to give better effect or achieve better fit.

crop marks Right-angle marks on artwork showing where the finished print is to be trimmed. Also called **tick marks** and **cut marks.**

cross direction Across the web of paper. Abbreviated to **CD.**

cross fold A fold at right angles to the direction of the web.

cross grain Used to denote that the grain of the paper in a book runs at right-angles to the spine, not parallel to it (which is preferable). Also used to refer to endpapers and external book covering materials when the grain of these components is at right angles to the spine. Also, **wrong-grain, short-grain** (in a book).

cross head A sub-heading ranged centrally over text. As distinct from a **boxed head** which is ranged left.

cross line screen The normal 45 degree half-tone screen used for standard half-tone origination.

cross-machine tension burst A paper break at the winding stage.

crossmarks See register marks.

cross sealer Blade in film wrapping machine which cuts and seals ends of wrapping.

crown Standard size of paper measuring 384 x 504mm (metric system).

crows footing The formation of ugly creases at the heads or feet of sections as they are folded. Often caused when heavy papers are folded and air is left trapped in the folds.

CRPU See **camera ready paste-up.**

CRT See **cathode ray tube.** Images of type are exposed on a CRT in a third generation phototypesetter.

crusher panel A rectangular, oval or circular panel area which is blocked on the spine or front of a book either **blind** (without ink or foil) or in colour. The title lettering is blocked on top of this panel. **crushing** See

crushing See **nipping.**

cryogenic Materials whose temperatures have been reduced as close as possible to absolute zero, usually as a means of reducing electrical resistance.

crystallisation Condition of an ink layer which will not accept a second ink overprinting.

CSWO Coldset web offset (q.v.).

CT See **chemical transfer**.

CTMP Chemi-thermomechanical pulp (q.v.).

C type Proprietary photographic process for producing continuous tone colour prints. Also, **C print**.

cumulative index An index which combines several other indices.

curl Sheet distortion leading to a tendency to roll up.

cursives Typefaces which simulate handwriting without joined characters.

cursor Movable indicator on a screen to show a location as instructed by the operator.

curtain coating A paper coating system in which the coating is injected horizontally across the web.

curved electros Electros shaped for use on rotary machines. Sometimes called **curved plates**.

customise In computing, to adapt and/or rewrite an existing program or routine to make it appropriate for a new and specific application.

custom software See **bespoke software**.

cut A block or engraving.

cut and paste In word processing and desktop publishing, the on-screen version of the manual task whereby areas of text or graphics are defined and stored for subsequent insertion into another area, page or file. Otherwise, in the context of repros, PMTs, and other hard-copy components, traditional camera paste-up methods.

cut-back binding See **adhesive binding**.

cut flush Binding style with the cover cut flush with the pages.

cut-in index Divisions cut into edge of book to indicate alphabetical steps.

cut-in notes Notes in an outside margin of a page but which the text runs round in some degree.

cut-line Mark left on negative or printed copy by failure to **spot out** a shadow left by an edge of patched-in artwork on CRC.

cut marks See **crop marks**.

cut-off The web press measure of length of sheet cut, usually determined by the plate cylinder circumference. Measured in inches or mm.

cut-out Illustration with background painted out or removed by process work.

cutscore Blade in die-cutting which scores for folding.

cut-size paper Small-sized paper sheets for stationery.

cutter Machine for cutting reels of paper into sheets. Four or more reels may be overlayed and cut simultaneously. Also, **precision cutter**.

cut-through index See **step index**.

cutting Sheeting web paper.

cutting ahead Cutting watermarked paper regardless of watermark positions. Compare **cut-to-register**.

cutting marks Marks on copy which indicate cutting lines.

cut-to-register Paper with a watermark in the same position on each cut sheet. Compare **cutting ahead**.

cwt Hundredweight. The **short cwt** (US) equals 100lbs, the **long cwt** (UK) equals 112lbs.

cyan The blue colour used in process printing.

cycle time The duration of a computer process relating to one storage location. Used to measure speed of performance.

cylinder 1. In computing, a set of **tracks** in a **disc pack** which are positioned vertically underneath each other. 2. In printing, the structure which carries the printing plate or blanket on the printing press.

cylinder dressing Sheets of paper around the impression cylinder of a letterpress printing machine which improve the definition of the print by providing a cushioned impression.

cylinder machine 1. See **cylinder mould machine**. 2. A letterpress printing machine which uses a revolving cylinder to make the impression. Also **cylinder press**.

cylinder mould machine A paper machine that makes high-quality **mould-made** paper by forming the paper on a cylindrical mould which revolves in the **stock**.

cylinder press Any letterpress printing machine which uses a cylinder to press the paper on the type. Compare **platen** press (q.v.).

cyrillic alphabet The Russian alphabet.

Аа Az	Ии Ishe	Рр Rzy	Шш Sha
Бб Buki	Йй Ishe s Kratkoi	Сс Slovo	Щщ Shcha
Вв Vyedi	Кк Kako	Тт Tvyerdo	Ъъ Tvyerdi Znak
Гг Glagol	Лл Lyudi	Уу U	Ыы Yeri
Дд Dobro	Мм Myslete	Фф Fiert	Ьь Myakhi Znak
Ее Yest	Нн Nash	Хх Kher	Ээ E
Жж Zhivete	Оо On	Цц Zy	Юю Yu
Зз Zemlya	Пп Pakoi	Чч Cha	Яя Ya

Illus 16. The cyrillic alphabet.

D

D See **Didot**.

dab out A quick method of examining the colour of an ink by dabbing a small amount of it on to the stock to be printed. Compare **draw down**.

dagger Dagger-shaped symbol used as a foot-note reference mark. Usually follows the asterisk in order of use.

dailies National daily newspapers.

daisy-chain bus Pertaining to polling circuits where a device will block the signal, indicating that it requires connection and may, once connected, modify the signal before passing it on to the next device.

daisy wheel Flat disc with characters on stalks used as the removable printing element of a letter-quality printer. Hence **daisy wheel printer**.

dampening solution or **damping solution** The fountain solution used in offset litho printing which consists of water and other chemical additives. In printing, the litho plate is first damped and then inked before printing takes place.

dampening system or **damping system** The system on a litho press whose function is to dampen the plate before it is inked. Typically it starts with a **fountain** in which the dampening solution resides. In the fountain rotates a **fountain roller** which gathers and meters down a uniform layer of the fountain solution on its surface. A cloth-covered **feed roller** moves intermittently to collect moisture from the fountain roller and transfer it across a gap to a metal **distributor roller** which meters the solution down to the **plate dampers** which dampen the plate itself.

damper Roller on a litho press which transfers moisture to the plate prior to inking.

dancer roller Roller on a web-offset press which controls the tension of the web.

dandy roll Cylinder on papermaking machine which impresses patterns and watermarks on the surface.

dandy sleeve A removable sleeve which can be fitted round a solid dandy roll to impress a particular watermark, and then be replaced with another after use. Also, **supported sleeve**.

dash Punctuation mark used either in the same way as parentheses, or to indicate an interruption, or to separate dates, numbers, etc. In typography a dash can be set as an **en rule** or as an **em rule** (q.v.).

-

–

—

Illus 17. A hyphen, an en rule and an em rule.

data Information in a computer store. A **database** or **data bank** is a collection of organised information from which categories may be selectively retrieved. **Data processing**, sometimes referred to as **DP**, is the generic term for the use of a computer to carry out business applications. **Data transmission** is the use of telecommunications to transfer information from one machine to another.

data bank A collection of data pertaining to a given subject or application.

database A collection of interrelated data that may be accessed by one or more application programs.

data communications The transmission and reception of data between remote devices, typically using the telephone lines or other dedicated data lines. Often abbreviated to **comms.** See also **data transmission**.

data compression A processing technique used to save space, especially in the storage of graphics information, by eliminating redundant data. It mainly involves eliminating gaps, identifying and coding strings of similar data, and suppressing all unnecessary extra data. Scan files for line artwork can be very successfully compressed to ratios as high as 20:1, since there are always many strings of similar data (whole strings of 0's to indicate black followed by whole strings of 1's to indicate white). Halftone information is much less easy to compress, and ratios are typically many times smaller than for line work.

data decompression The functional reverse to **data compression**, involving the building back of compressed data to full file length.

dataline Leased line dedicated to the transmission of data. Datalines can be either low-speed or high-speed, supporting transmission of different speeds.

data link The medium employed to connect to remote devices such as a telephone line.

data transfer The transfer of electronic data from one machine to another by such means as **media conversion, data communications,** or **OCR.**

data transfer rate The number of bytes (or bits) per given unit of time that pass between devices. See also **baud.**

data transmission The transfer of data from one point to another by one or other form of dataline - private leased-line, **PSTN** service, etc. To transfer data successfully from one machine to another, a set of common **protocols** must be followed at both the transmitting end and the receiving end. The chief amongst these are: **serial** or **parallel** transmission; **synchronous** or **asynchronous** mode; **full-duplex** or **half-duplex**; and a declaration of the **baud** rate (speed). A typical specification for data transmission between one pc and another might be, for example: serial transmission; asynchronous; full-duplex; 1200 baud.

data validation The process of checking that data corresponds to agreed criteria.

day glow Proprietary name for fluorescent inks.

DCE Data Circuit-Terminating Equipment A modem or printer in the context of data transmission. Interfaces possible in data transmission are **DTE** (Data Terminal Equipment, ie. computers or terminals) to **DCE** (ie. modems or printers); or **DTE** to **DTE.** See **DTE.**

DD Double density (in referring to a disc's formatting capacity). Compare **HD.** See also **disc.**

DDL Imagen's **Document Description Language.** One of several **page description languages** now largely displaced by PostScript.

dead matter Type which is finished with or which will not be used, and may be 'killed'.

dead metal Non-printing areas on a letterpress metal printing plate.

dead white A white with no modelling tint.

de-archive The retrieval of files held on backing store and placing them on a system disc.

debarking Stripping bark from logs prior to their being pulped.

debris Used to describe paper dust or edge dust which finds its way on to the offset printing blanket.

debugging The detection and correction of errors in a computer program before it goes into use.

decentralised computer network One in which certain control functions are distributed among several network nodes.

deciduous trees Hardwood trees which shed their leaves annually.

deck Term used in multi-unit web offset imposition, where a section is being formed from running one web under another into the folder. After **cut-off** the two sheets are folded together to form a section (typically two 16pp sheets folded one inside the other to yield one 32pp section). 'A' deck is the top side of the top web, and 'B' deck is the lower side of the top web; 'C' deck is the top side of the lower web, and 'D' deck is the lower side of the lower web. Colour locations may appear in different positions according to the configuration used. See **colour fall**.

deckle The width of a paper-making machine's web. **Deckle boards** retain the stock on the wire. **Deckle edge** is the untrimmed feathering edge of paper. **Deckle frame** is the rectangular frame which contains the stock on the wire in hand-made paper.

decoder A logic component the purpose of which is to convert data from one numeric system to another - binary to hexadecimal, for example.

decoding The computer process of interpreting instruction codes.

dedicated An item of equipment or electronics used for only one type of application and maybe only running one program.

dedication Inscription by the author dedicating a book to an individual. Carried among the **prelims** (q.v.).

deep-etch half-tone A halftone in which all the smaller highlight dots have been removed to leave plain white. Also **drop-out half-tone**.

deep-etch plate Litho printing plate made from positive film in which the printing areas are recessed below the surface. Used for long runs.

deep-sea markets Term used by the paper trade to indicate Far Eastern and other markets whose distance from home can mean that special terms and deals can be struck without affect on domestic trade.

default In computing, the parameters defined by the designer or programmer as a standard setting that will be used in the absence of any alternative input by a user.

definition The degree of detail and sharpness in a reproduction.

degradation The deterioration of communications signal characteristics.

dehumidification Removal of humidity from the air.

deinking Removing ink and other unwanted chemicals from printed wastepaper to recover and re-use fibre content.

del Delete. Proof reader's instruction to erase text or other matter.

delamination Separation of surface from paper by ink tack or separation of film laminate from its substrate, often caused by impurities trapped between the film and the substrate.

delimiter Character used to denote the limit of a computer field.

demographic edition Edition of a publication designed for a specifically targeted sector of the readership with advertising limited to that edition.

demurrage In seafreight, the charges incurred when a vessel is held longer at the port for unloading than the time allowed or in other ways is delayed in leaving.

demy Standard size of paper 444 x 564mm (metric system).

density 1. Measurement of the tonal value of a printed or photographic area. Density is the light-stopping, or light-absorbing, ability of an object. In mathematical terms it is the reciprocal (opposite) of transmission or reflection, and it is measured by the formula, incident light divided by transmitted (or reflected) light expressed as a logarithmic value (power of 10). Logarithmic values are chosen to reflect the fact that perceived density proceeds in steps of 'twice as much as last time', not linearly. In practice this means a measuring scale of 0.0 at the lightest end of a subject measured by a densitometer (100% transmission/reflection of light) up to 3.0 at the farthest end (0.1% transmission/reflection of light). 2. In computing, a measure of capacity used for disc storage. Most pc discs are **double density** or **high density**. See **disc**.

density range The range of contrast between the lightest area and the darkest area of a piece of artwork or photograph (see **density**). A good transmission density range in a transparency for reproduction should be between 1.8 to 2.4, with no less than 0.3 in the highlights and no more than 2.7 in the shadows as the outer parameters.

densometer Instrument that measures the air resistance of an area of paper.

DENSY A typesetter-command language used for some brands of Linotype photosetter.

depth gauge 1. Micrometer for measuring etching depth on plates. 2. Typographical ruler for measuring **line feed** (q.v.).

depth of field Area which remains in focus between close and distant objects in a photograph.

dermatitis Skin disease with symptoms of itchy rash caused by some of the chemicals used in printing.

descender The part of a character which descends below the base line or x-height, e.g. y and p.

descreening The elimination of the screen in a printed halftone, normally when it is to be reproduced to a different size. The screen pattern is destroyed either by electronic 'blurring', or photographically by reduction and refocussing.

desensitise Treat an offset plate with gum arabic or a desensitising plate etch to ensure that the non-image areas do not retain ink, and do attract water.

designation marks Identifying letters at the foot of each signature of a book which confirm the sequence. See also **signature**.

desktop publishing The production of fully made-up pages using a micro with a graphics-oriented **wysiwyg** page make-up package for assembling the components of the page, and a **laser printer** for generating the output repro. See illustration overleaf.

develop Use chemical or other process to produce an image on photographic paper or a printing plate.

developer Material used to remove unexposed coating on a litho plate.

device control A transmission code that may be used to control a hardware device.

diacriticals Marks above and below letters, such as accents or the cedilla.

diagnosics Programs designed to trace faults in a system or program.

diamond Obsolete term for $4^{1}/_{2}$ pt type.

DIANE Acronym for Direct Access Network for Europe, an on-line information service developed by the Commission of European Communities.

diaresis Two dots over a vowel to indicate stress.

diazo A chemical coating in photography or platemaking and the term given to a copying process which uses light-sensitive compounds (diazonium). See also **blueprints**.

dictionary A file used by a word processor or front-end system to check

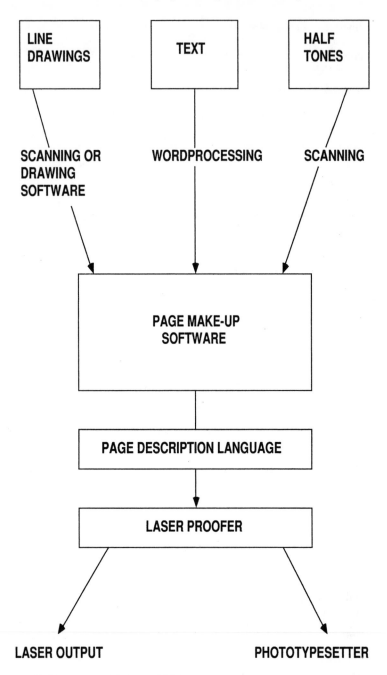

Illus 18. The concept of desktop publishing.

spelling or hyphenation. A dictionary can be a **true dictionary**, which contains all words which can be hyphenated with their hyphenation points, or an **exception dictionary** which lists only exceptions to logical rules, and is used to hyphenate words in conjunction with a **hyphenation logic** program.

Didone Group of typefaces previously known as **Modern**, e.g. Bodoni.

Didot The European measure of type. Based on a point of 0.376mm (0.0148"). Abbreviated to **D**.

diecase Monotype matrix case.

die-cutting The cutting of paper or card with steel rules on a press to give cut-outs or folds in printed material.

die stamping An **intaglio** (q.v.) printing process from a steel die giving a relief surface on the paper.

diffuse reflection Scattering of light away from a surface.

diffusion transfer See **photomechanical transfer**.

digest Condensed version of other textual work.

digester The container in a chemical pulping system in which wood is processed with chemicals to extract the fibres.

digest-size A page size the same as *Reader's Digest*, i.e. 5 inches by 7 inches.

digipad Input device on which drawn images are digitised and displayed on a VDU and/or stored in memory.

digit A character that represents a whole number.

digital Representation of data by digits.

digital camera Name sometimes used to describe a flatbed scanner, typically for monochrome subjects.

digital computer Computer which uses numbers to represent and manipulate data.

digital fount Electonically stored **fount** in which the characters are stored as computer instructions for the typesetting machine rather than in any physical, visible form. The instructions can be in **bitmap** form or **vector** form. In bitmap form, the shapes are held by the computer as x/y co-ordinated grids of pixels; in vector form they are held as outline shapes which are then filled in by the computer after the outline has first been generated. Vector representation is starting to supplant bitmap representation.

digital halftone A halftone with a screen pattern generated by computer in emulation of the traditional halftone screen pattern, rather than achieved optically via a camera and physical screen.

digital map See **bit map**.

digital proofing Name given to any technique of proofing generated by computer rather than from a physical object such as a film or bromide. Examples include laser proofing text, or the **soft proofing** of illustration scans by display on a VDU screen.

digital-to-analogue converter A device that converts a digital value to a corresponding analogue form. Compare **analogue-to-digital converter (ADC)**.

digitise To scan a subject and place the information into a computer memory for subsequent regeneration.

digitiser A graphic input device such as a monochrome flatbed scanner which scans an image and stores it in memory for re-use.

dilitho See **direct litho**.

dimension To define the parameters of an array in programming.

dimensional stability Ability of paper to retain its shape despite variations in moisture content or mechanical stress.

dimension marks Marks on camera copy indicating the area of a reduction or enlargement.

DIN Deutsche Industrie Norme. The German standards institute. DIN paper sizes, now renamed **ISO** (q.v.) have been adopted as the European standard. See also **A series**.

dingbat Ornament, symbol, printer's decoration.

❑ ✿▲✾✳✲●☽✛✴✳❑❑✿◆❙▼❑✸❒❑▮✳✧✿❍◯ℰ✎✆
Illus 19. Some typical dingbats.

diode In electronics, a device that has a low electrical resistance in one direction but a high resistance in the other, thus allowing current to pass only in one direction. **Photodiodes** (q.v.) used in scanners are diodes sensitive to light, whose conductivity varies with the intensity of the light falling on it.

dioxins Highly toxic chlorine compounds, said to be found in trace amounts both in the effluent water from the chlorine bleaching process, and in the air when chlorine-bleached papers are burned.

DIP De-inked pulp.

dip coating Coating method in which the web is passed around a roller immersed in coating solution.

diphthong Letters placed together as in œ, æ, etc. Contrast **ligature**.

direct access Use of storage medium which can access information without the need for sequential searching, e.g. a disc as compared with a cassette.

direct approach platen Press on which the platen approaches the forme on a parallel plane with it.

direct-duplicating film See **autopositive film**.

direct entry phototypesetter Self-contained phototypesetter with its own keyboard, CPU and output device.

direct impression Typewriter-type setting in which the image is created by direct impression from a type character, e.g. an IBM Composer. Also called **strike-on composition**.

direct input Term used to describe journalists keying copy directly for typesetting using modified word-processing equipment, rather than producing hard-copy destined for rekeying by a keyboard operator.

direction of travel Direction in which web moves through a paper machine or press.

direct litho Litho press system which transfers the image direct from the printing plate without offsetting it to a blanket first.

directory An index file containing details of all other files held on disc.

direct screening Reproduction process in which copy is separated and screened in one step. As distinct from **indirect screening** where a scanner output unit produces continuous-tone films which are then contacted through a half-tone screen to produce final **hard-dot positives**.

dirty 1. Typesetting with many errors introduced at the keyboard. 2. Copy with many handwritten amendments.

disc 1. Circular glass typefount used in some second generation photosetters. 2. Computer storage device available in various sizes and giving direct access to the information it contains. Data is stored on a disc in a series of concentric circular **tracks**, each of which is divided into a number of **sectors**. A typical format for a microcomputer disc might be 80 tracks per side, 2 sides, with 9 sectors per track. On each sector, the data can be written in differing degrees of **density**. A **double-density DD** 3.5 inch disc holds 80 tracks per side, 2 sides, 9 sectors per track; and at a recording density of 0.5Kb per sector, therefore holds a total of 720Kb (around 110,000 words). A **high-density HD** disc might be recorded at 80 tracks per side, 2 sides, 15 sectors per track, making a total capacity of 1.2Mb (around 175,000 words).

disc cartridge A portable hard disc contained within a protective casing that may be loaded on to a disc drive.

disc conversion See **media conversion**.

disc crash A hardware or software malfunction resulting in an inability to access the contents of a disc.

disc drive A device which writes information to or reads information from a magnetic disc. See **disc**.

disc operating system (DOS) In computing, the operating system which controls how input/output routines are handled by the computer.

disc pack A set of discs mounted on a common spindle. Each disc is a thin metal rigid platter coated on both sides with a magnetic material (typically ferrous oxide). The surface is divided into **tracks** (concentric rings) and each track is divided into **sectors** (subdivisions of the tracks). Data is recorded as magnetised spots along each track, and is accessed by **read-write** heads.

disc refiner Machine which refines pulp by rubbing fibres between vertical rotating discs.

discrete In computing, describes items or processes which are separate and distinct, each unattached to any others.

discretionary hyphens Hyphenation points for words, either held in the **hypenation exception dictionary** of a front-end system or introduced while keyboarding new text. They indicate where a word may be broken if it needs to be hyphenated at the end of a line. Discretionary hyphens will overrule any logical hyphenation program in use.

disc ruling A method of ruling stationery with metal discs.

diskette See **floppy disc.**

display ads Advertisements 'displayed' to occupy part or all of a page rather than set in columns.

display character generator A component of a VDU that converts input signals into those that define the character shape on the screen.

display face A type face designed for **display sizes** rather than for **composition sizes** (q.v.).

display matter Typography set and displayed so as to be distinguished from the text, e.g. headings. Hence **display sizes** are sizes of type from 14pt upwards. **Display advertisements** are those using display type for presentational purposes.

display papers and boards Papers and boards used for point-of-sale or exhibition purposes.

display sizes Sizes of type larger than 14pt, i.e. used for display rather than text.

18pt   24pt   30pt   36pt

48pt

60pt

72pt

Illus 20. Common sizes of display type.

display tube See **cathode ray tube.**

diss Distribute. Return letterpress type to the case after printing.

dissolving pulp Highly processed and pure chemical pulp.

distributing rollers Generic term for the main train of rollers in the **ink pyramid** of a litho press which meter and distribute the ink downwards to the **plate inkers.**

distribution See **diss.**

distributor roller Large-diameter roller in the centre of a litho **dampening system** which takes the moisture strip from the feed roller and distributes it down to the **plate dampers.**

dithering Method of simulating grey on a screen or print by spacing out the number of dots created in a given area to give the illusion of tone.

ditto Typographic symbol for 'repeat the above matter'. Set as ".

document reader A device that can read a document into a computer. See **intelligent character recognition, optical character recognition, magnetic ink character recognition.**

dodge To block light from selected areas while making a photograph print in order to bring out detail.

dog-eared pages Corners of pages that are inadvertently folded over during processing. When the book is trimmed and the corners corrected the untrimmed portions protrude.

dongle A hardware component sold with a software package and without which the package is rendered unusable. The dongle is inserted into the computer's serial port, external expansion port or internal expansion slot.

DOS See **disc operating system.**

dot 1. The individual element from which a halftone reproduction is made up. 2. Synonym for **pixel** (q.v.) or **spot;** the smallest resolvable image which can be displayed by any particular system on a screen or on hard copy (bromide, film). Dots per inch - **dpi** - is the standard measure of resolution, expressed as dots or pixels, for fourth-generation imagesetters and laser printers. The finer the resolution (the more dots per inch), the crisper the finished image.

dot etching Colour correcting on screened colour separations by changing the size of the dots by hand etching to change tonal balance.

dot for dot Reproduction of an already screened half-tone by photographing it as if it were fine line.

dot gain The enlargement of the half-tone dot which occurs during the mechanical processes of printing.

dot-generator programs The programs in the output unit of a scanner or imagesetter which analyse the scanned data and, in the case of tone images, convert the data into an output pattern of halftone dots. Each halftone dot is built up from a large number of underlying pixels or dots at the given resolution of the output unit. A low-resolution output unit has a smaller number of pixels at its disposal, and so can generate effectively only coarse-screen (large-dot) halftones such as 65-screen or below. A fine-resolution device (2540dpi and beyond) can generate effectively fine-screen halftones up to 150-screen and beyond.

dotless i An 'i' available in some photocomposition founts for the purpose of accommodating ligatures.

dot matrix Patterns of dots used to create images on screen or printer.

dot matrix printer A computer printer which forms its printed characters from a pattern of dots. Most dot-matrix printers are either 9-pin, 18-pin, or 24-pin models, which describe the number of pins held on the vertical matrix which forms the letters. The more dots the sharper the letters. Typical **resolutions for** a 24-pin dot-matrix printer are 120dpi in draft, 360dpi in letter-quality. Typical printing speeds are 180cps in draft, 60cps in letter-quality.

dot slurring Elongation of dots at their trailing edges.

dot spread Unacceptably enlarged dot size formation during printing.

double In printing, an unwanted second image fringing the first, correct image. Typically caused by a machine fault, or an excess of mechanical speed, or incorrect blanket settings. Also called a **slur**.

double black In printing four-colour process illustrations and heavy black solids together, refers to printing the black twice : once for the the halftone, and once for the solid. Permits better control of ink weight and **tracking** (q.v.).

double-black duotone A duotone created from two black plates and printed once in conventional black and once in a toned black or grey. Used in very high quality work to extend the tonal range available.

double burn An exposure of two or more images on to a single film or plate to create one composite image. Often applies to half-tone films which are held on a separate foil from line films : the two sets of foils are printed down on to plate as separate operations.

double case A type case combining upper and lower case.

double-coated Coated paper which is given two coats either side instead of the normal one coat. Gives increased smoothness and consistency to the sheet.

double-density disc A micro computer storage disc which can store twice as much information as its 'single density' counterpart. Abbreviated **DD**. See **disc**.

double dot half-tone Two half-tone negatives exposed into a combination image on a plate to give greater clarity to the highlights and shadows (on one neg) and the middle-tones (on the other).

double-duty envelope Envelope which can be re-used by the recipient.

double elephant Drawing paper measuring 27 x 40 inches.

double exposure Two images superimposed on one another to form one.

double-page spread Facing pages in a book or periodical.

double printing Two exposures in register from separate half-tones.

double roll A second press roll over the printing surface when extra inking is required.

double-sided discs Discs which can store information on both sides. For micro computers, double-sided discs are the norm.

double spread Print going across two facing pages.

double-tone half-tone A colour plate printed slightly out of register to create a duotone effect.

double tone ink A printing ink which creates an extra tone on drying, due to spreading.

doubling A second out-of-register image produced during a single impression. Caused by the ink on the blanket remaining wet after impression and transferring back from the blanket cylinder to the following sheet. If the following sheet is out of register it appears as a double image – doubling.

doughnut hickey A **hickey** (q.v.) with a white 'halo' around it.

dow etching A powderless etching technique for letterpress plates invented by Dow Chemical Corporation.

download Copy across data from one computer to another.

downloadable founts Founts which can be sent to a laser printer's memory from an outside storage source (typically a disc) rather than being supplied resident in **ROM** or available from a plug-in cartridge (**hard fount**).

down-time Non-productive time when a printing machine is being maintained or made ready.

dpi Dots per inch. A measurement of **resolution** (q.v.) associated with output devices using laser imaging techniques.

DPS See **double page spread**.

draft quality output Low-quality high-speed wp printer output from dot-matrix printer. See also **NLQ, letter quality**.

dragon's blood A red powder used for protecting side walls from under-biting during the etching of letterpress plates.

drainability The rate at which paper stock parts with water when drained.

draw down A thin film of ink spread on paper with a spatula to evaluate its shade.

draw-in Binding method in which the section threads are pulled through cover boards and glued.

drawn-on cover A binding style in which the cover is glued directly on to the spine. Also known as **wrappered**.

dressing 1. The range of typefaces held on a photosetter. 2. Putting the typefaces in a photosetter.

drier A mechanical device, such as a gas oven, used to dry ink on 'heatset' web machines.

driers Additives in printing ink such as cobalt, manganese and resinates, which accelerate drying.

drilling Perforating a pile of sheets with holes for special binding methods, such as loose-leaf.

driography Litho platemaking process in which the non-image areas are silicone rubber.

drive out To set text with wide word spacing deliberately to increase the number of lines it occupies.

driver Computer routine which handles communication between CPU and peripherals. In typesetting, a program which controls a printer or a typesetter (**printer driver, typesetter driver**).

drop cap(s) Drop capital. A letter or letters at the beginning of a paragraph which extend beyond the depth of the rest of the text line. Also called **drop initial(s)**. Compare **cocked up initial**.

A T one time the Fox and the Stork were on visiting terms and seemed very good friends. So the Fox invited the Stork

Illus 21. A drop cap or drop initial.

drop guides Guides on a printing machine which position the sheet ready for the grippers.

drop heads See **dropped heads**.

drop initial See **drop cap(s)**.

drop-out blue Light blue, invisible to monochrome litho film. Useful for **grids**, marks on artwork, etc. Also known as **non-reproducing blue**.

drop-out half-tone Half-tone in which the highlight areas have no screen dots and simply show the white of the paper. Also known as a **deep-etch halftone**.

dropped heads Chapter headings positioned a few lines below the top of full text pages.

dross The surface skin on molten type metal.

drum An obsolescent computer storage medium using a rotating magnetic drum.

drum printer A line printing device containing a drum on which each printable character forms a complete row across the drum surface. As every occurrence of a particular character in a line is printed simultaneously, printing rate is considerably enhanced.

drum scanner Scanner with cylindrical platen for mounting transparencies to be scanned, as distinct from a **flatbed** scanner.

dry back The loss of gloss of an ink as it dries.

dry creping See **creping**.

dry end The part of a Fourdrinier paper machine which comprises the **dryer section** and the **calender section**.

dryer section Section of a Fourdrinier paper machine which consists of a series of large steam-heated drying cylinders which dry the paper web.

dry indicator size test Method of measuring paper's water resistance. See also **Cobb size test**.

drying section The last part of the papermaking machine, after the **press section**, which completes the drying of the web.

drying time Time taken for the ink on a printed sheet to dry enough for further work to be done on the sheet, e.g. binding or extra printing.

dry-mounting A method of photographic mounting which uses pressure-sensitive backing.

dry offset See **letterset**.

dry picking resistance The picking resistance of paper in dry conditions.

dry proof Cromalin or other plastic proof of an illustration as distinct from a **wet proof** (q.v.) involving machine plates.

dry pulp Pulp in dry sheets as distinct from **slush pulp** (q.v.).

dry transfer lettering Sheets of typographic characters which can be transferred on to paper by rubbing.

dry-up See **scumming**.

D/S Double sided (of a disc, or of a printing plate).

DTD Document Type Definition. One of the principal declarations in the structuring of an **SGML** document (q.v.).

DTE Data Terminal Equipment A computer or terminal in the context of data transmission. See **DCE**.

DTP See **desktop publishing**.

dual binding An edition of a book which is bound partly in paperback and partly in hardback. The same folded and gathered sheets are used.

duct Ink trough on a printing press. The **duct roller** revolves in the duct to regulate the amount of ink released. See **inking system**.

dues Orders for a new publication, new edition or reprint which accrue before the book is available. Publishers record such orders and supply them as soon as stock is available.

dull finish enamel An enamel paper with a low gloss.

dummy Mock-up of a book or other piece of printing to indicate specifications.

dump Transfer a computer file into or out of storage.

dumpbin Point of sale low, open container for the easy stacking and display of goods.

duoformer The duoformer paper machine has an additional wire running on top of the normal machine wire, which draws water from the topside of the web, producing an evenly formed sheet. As distinct from the **twin-wire** process (q.v.), which has two separate webs of paper which are brought together before pressing.

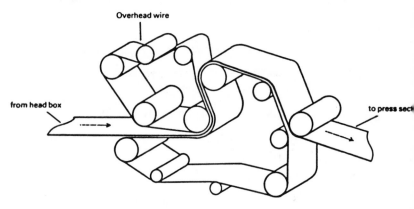

Illus 22. A duoformer.

duotone A two-colour half-tone produced from a single-colour original. The two negatives are made at different screen angles - typically 45^0 and 15^0 - and to different contrast ranges. See also **fake duotone**.

dupe See duplicate block.

duplex A linecasting matrix with two character moulds.

duplex cutter A sheeting device which cuts two different sheet lengths from the web simultaneously.

duplex half-tone See **duotone**.

duplex paper Paper with a different colour on each side.

duplicate block, film, transparency plate, etc. More than one identical item produced from the same original. Used for printing several copies 'up' on a machine, printing in two locations, or for other purposes.

duplicator Small office machine for short-run reproduction from a stencil.

duplicator paper Special absorbent paper for duplicating from a stencil master.

dusting Accumulation of powdered paper on the non-printing areas of a blanket.

dust jacket Paper wrapper of a book carrying the title and author's name.

Dutch grey board See **grey board**.

Dvorak Keyboard layout in which the keys are positioned so as to be most readily accessible to the fingers which most often use them. Contrast **azerty, qwerty**.

dye A soluble colouring matter (pigments are insoluble).

dyed through In bookbinding, a dyed-through cloth is dyed on both sides, not just on the surface. Contrast **whiteback**.

dyeline prints or **dyelines** See **blueprints**.

dye mask Special sort of colour film used when colour separating transparencies by camera to assist with colour correction. See also **masking, trimask**.

dye transfer Photographic process producing colour prints with dyes which are selectively absorbed.

Dylux Proprietary name for double-sided light-sensitive proofing paper.

dynamic allocation Assignment of operating system resources to a program at the time of execution rather than at the point that the program is loaded.

dynamic memory Computer memory that will degrade in time if a power source is not permanently or frequently applied.

E

E13B Magnetic ink fount used on cheques.

EAN European Article Number. See **bar code**.

e&oe Errors and omissions excepted: a caveat often printed on quotations or invoices.

earlies The advance copies sent by the binder to the publisher ahead of the main delivery, and used for checking and/or early promotion. Also, **advance copies**.

earmark Particular characteristic or feature of a typeface which distinguishes it from all others and assists recognition.

earpieces Small advertisements on either side of a newspaper's mast-head.

easer Printing ink additive used to reduce tack.

EBCDIC Extended Binary Coded Decimal Information Code. The code used by IBM mainframe computers.

edgeboard connector The most common method of connecting add-on printed circuit boards to computer hardware.

edge cutters Waterjets on a paper machine which 'clean off' the edges of the web on the wire.

edge decoration Coloured dyes, marbling transfers or gilding on trimmed book edges.

edge gilding Gold-leaf edging on a book.

edge tear Broken edge of web.

edge tearing resistance Resistance of paper to the further development of a small edge tear.

edit Check, arrange and correct data or copy before final presentation.

editing terminal Visual display unit capable of retrieving a file and editing the contents prior to processing.

edition All the copies of a printed work from the same set of type or plates.

edition binding Conventional, production-line, casebound binding.

editor 1. Publisher's employee who corrects and modifies original manuscripts to prepare them for subsequent publication. 2. A software utility employed to aid the production and modification of source programs.

editorial 1. Publication's formal views on a subject expressed in a special column. 2. The editorial matter (as distinct from advertisements) in a publication.

educational contractor A wholesaler who specialises in supplying books for schools.

EELs Measurements indicating the **opacity** (q.v.) of paper read by means of an EEL Opacimeter. Compare **Elrepho** measurements.

EFL English as a Foreign Language. An important book publishing area for many English-language publishers. As distinct from **ELT** (q.v.).

EGA Enhanced graphics adapter. Driver for superior graphics monitor. See also **CGA, VGA.**

eggshell antique Bulky paper with a slightly mottled surface, like that of an egg.

Egyptian Type style with a squared serif.

abcdefghijklmnopqrstuvwxyz
ABCDEFGHIJKLMNOPQRSTUVWXYZ

Illus 23. Egyptian typeface.

eight-bit micro A micro which reads and manipulates data in 'words' (units) of eight bits long. See also **sixteen-bit micro, thirty-two bit micro.**

Ektachrome Alternative name for **transparency.**

electro Electrotype. Duplicate of block or forme made by coating a mould with copper and nickel.

electron gun See **gun.**

electronic colour retouching The ability to alter local areas of a scanned colour subject by defining and then amending them electronically. Available on most **epc** systems.

electronic composition Computer-assisted typesetting and page make-up.

electronic dot generation The ability of an output scanner to generate half-tone dots directly on the output medium in a variety of screen rulings and forms.

electronic engraving Letterpress block engraving with a stylus controlled by a light sensitive cell scanning the original.

electronic mail The transfer of documents or messages between computers or word processors using direct links, telecommunications or satellites. A typical electronic mail system comprises a central 'postbox' computer connected via modems and ordinary telephone lines to subsribers' personal computers or other computer terminals. Each subscriber is given a personal mailbox number – the address to which his messages are sent and stored in the central computer. A subscriber who wishes to send a message to another subscriber sends his message from his pc to the central postbox computer, quoting the mailbox number of the adressee. When the recipient next dials up to the system, he is informed that a message is waiting in his mailbox, which he can then call down to his computer.

electronic mark-up Generic typesetting codes inserted into a text being sent on disc or down the wire, which identify headings, different levels of text, etc. The generic codes can be converted into typesetter commands by means of a look-up table at the time of output. See also **generic coding** and **ASPIC**.

electronic page composition system An **epc** electronic page composition system is one which comprises a series of interlinked computers based on colour scanners. The complete range of processes encompassed by a large electronic page composition system comprise the colour scanning of originals, retouching and colour correction, soft proofing, the scanning-in or direct entry of text, masking and page assembly, tint laying, and final output of one-piece imposed page films in four colours, or press-ready printing plates.

electronic pen See **light pen**.

electronic printer Portmanteau word to describe any plain-paper printer such as a laser printer or similar using fourth-generation technology or later.

electronic scanner 1. Machine which scans full-colour copy wrapped around a drum and, by reading colour densities, produces separations. 2. Device on a printing press or paper machine which sends control readings back to a console or to the machine itself.

electronic slanting Creation of a slanted roman typeface by a photosetter or laser printer to imitate italics.

electronic spreadsheet. See **spreadsheet.**

electrophotography The use of **electrostatic** (q.v.) forces to copy images, as in photocopiers.

electrostatic plates Small offset plates made by electrostatic printing processes.

electrostatic printing Copying process involving the reflection of light from an original on to an electrically charged drum. Areas affected by the light lose their charge. **Toner,** retained by the charged areas, is fused to the paper, thereby creating an image. Also, **xerography, xerographic printing.** Laser printers use this principle for output.

electrotype Duplicate of block or forme made by coating a mould with metal.

elision The omission of a part considered unnecessary, particularly in numbers, eg the omission of the second '12' in the statement pp120-3.

elite Small size of typewriter type: 12 characters per inch. **Microelite** has 15 characters per inch; **pica** has 10 characters per inch.

ellipsis Three dots (. . .) indicating an omission.

elliptical dot Elongated dot giving a smoother gradation of tone in middle-tones. Other dot formations in common use include round, rectangular, pincushion.

Elrepho Percentages 'Elrepho' are used to quantify the **opacity** (q.v.) of a paper using a Zeiss Elrepho machine. See also **EELs,** which are measurements of opacity taken using an EEL Opacimeter.

elrod Letterpress casting machine for rules and leads.

ELT English Language Teaching. An important books publishing area for many English language publishers. See also **EFL** – English as a Foreign Language.

em 1. Width of the body of the lower case 'm' in any typeface. 2. Standard unit of measurement (also called 'pica'). One em equals 0.166044 inches.

email See **electronic mail.**

embossed finish Surface pattern pressed in paper.

embossing See **blocking.**

emerald Obsolete type size of about $6^{1}/_{2}$ pt.

em rule A horizontal rule the width of an em of the fount being set. The em rule is used in the same sense as parentheses, or to indicate an interruption.

emulation The imitation of one system's code-set by another such that the two may communicate.

emulator A program that permits a computer to imitate a different system.

emulsification Dispersing of water into another liquid, e.g. when water 'bleeds' into the ink on a litho press and degrades the density of the image.

emulsion Photosensitive coating on film or plate. Hence, **emulsion side**.

en Half the width of an **em** (q.v.). The width of the average type character, so is used as the basic unit of measurement for casting off copy. Also **character** or **keystroke**, in the sense of **ens per hour** (= characters set in one hour) or **ens of setting** (= character count in a manuscript).

enamel paper Paper coated on one side with a very high finish.

encapsulated PostScript A subset of **PostScript** addressing the file description of illustrations and graphic material. In some circumstances a useful 'standard' format for the transfer of illustration files from one system to another. As a file format often referred to as **EPSF**.

enclosure Contents of mail shot.

encode To code groups of characters.

end or **end leaf** See **endpaper**.

endmatter The final parts of a book after the main text: appendices, notes, index, etc. Also, **backmatter**.

endnotes Notes which come at the end of a chapter or at the back of the book rather than appearing as **footnotes** on the pages where the text references fall.

end of file (EOF) The physical termination point of an amount of data or the mark used to indicate this point.

end-of-line decisions Decisions on hyphenation or justification made either by the operator or automatically by the typesetting system.

endpaper Strong paper used for securing the body of a book to its case. Endpapers may be plain, coloured, marbled, etc. and should be specified with the **grain direction** (q.v.) parallel to the spine.

endsheets Endpapers (US).

engine-sized pulp See **beater-sized pulp.**

engine sizing Adding size to paper in the early stages of stock preparation. Also called **internal sizing.** Internal size is applied to increase a paper's resistance to water absorption, and may be either the mildly acidic alum/rosin formulation, or a neutral synthetic size, chemically produced. **External size** is distinct from this: it is added at the **size press** (q.v.) on the papermaking machine, and typically consists of starch.

English Obsolete type size, approximately 14pt.

English finish Smoothly calendered book paper.

engraving 1. Printing plate etched for use in letterpress. 2. Print made from such a plate.

engraved blanket A lowering of the blanket surface in the areas of printing due to harmful ingredients in the ink.

enhanced word processing Word processing which falls somewhere between traditional wp offerings and DTP.

ennage The number of characters in a piece of copy or setting. An **en** is used to mean any single character.

enp In papermaking, extended nip press: a new, extended, style of roller system which comes between the wet end and the start of the dry end on the papermaking machine which aids formation and drying.

en rule A horizontal rule or dash the width of an **en** of the fount being set. The en rule separates dates, numbers, lists; and is sometimes used (in place of the **em rule**) in the same sense as parentheses. Contrast **em rule.**

ens of setting Just the number of characters and spaces in the text of a piece of setting, as opposed to the total number of **keystrokes** (characters and spaces plus codes) in the piece.

envelope paper Paper made for high-speed envelope die-cutting machines.

envelope-stuffer Mail-shot promoting or advertising products or services, sent out in an envelope.

environment In personal computing, the screen presentation of information, and keyboard access to it (the **user interface**). User-friendly environments concentrate on the pictorial representation of instructions (see **WIMP**). More traditional environments require knowledge of the operating system's particular commands and conventions (e.g. **MS-DOS**).

EOL End of line.

EOT End of tape.

epc system Electronic page composition system (q.v.).

epigraph Quotation in book prelims or at the start of a chapter.

epilogue Closing section at the end of a novel or play.

EPROM Erasable Programmable Read Only Memory. May be overwritten with special equipment. See **ROM, PROM, firmware**.

EPSF Encapsulated PostScript format. See **encapsulated PostScript**.

equilibrium moisture content Moisture content of paper at same relative humidity as its environment. Hence also, **equilibrium relative humidity**.

erasable storage Storage medium that can be erased and reused as required, e.g. a floppy disc.

ergonomics The study of equipment design in the context of man/machine interface, with the express purpose of reducing operator fatigue and discomfort, and to ensure maximum operating conditions.

erh Equilibrium relative humidity: the relative humidity of a substance stabilised with the ambient conditions.

erratum slip Slip of paper inserted or pasted into a book and containing list of author's post-press corrections.

escalator clause Clause in a royalty contract that allows for the author to earn at a higher rate once a certain number of sales have been achieved.

esparto Long-fibred grass used in pulp for paper-making.

esquisse Rough layout or design.

etch To produce a printing plate by chemical removal of non-printing areas. **Etching ink** protects the plate from the etching solution.

etching 1. See **colour etching**. 2. Form of print created by cutting the image into a specially coated plate using acid.

Ethernet A local area network (**LAN**) developed by the Xerox Corporation, Digital Equipment Corporation and Intel Corporation. Unlike the

Cambridge Ring style of LAN, the Ethernet is a straight-line network: each item of equipment is connected to the Ether, a cable, by means of a **transceiver** device. There is a **terminator** at each end of the Ether line.

Euronet Packet switched data communications network specified by the European commission to link countries in the European community and others.

European Article Number EAN See **bar code.**

even pages Left-hand, or verso, pages, with even numbers.

even small caps Small capitals without full capitals.

even working A total of pages in a publication which can be produced entirely by printing sections of the same numbers of pages (16s, 32s, etc.). See also **oddment.**

everdamp paper Transfer paper for laying down images on lithographic plates.

exception dictionary Computer store of words which do not hyphenate in accordance with the machine's rules of logic. See also **hyphenation exception dictionary** and **discretionary hyphen.**

exclusive type area Type area exclusive of headline and folio. The type area inclusive of headline and folio is known as the **inclusive type area** (q.v.).

execute The process of interpreting and carrying out a computer function.

expanded type Typeface with characters wider than the normal fount.

abcdefghijklmnopqrstuvwxyz ABCDEFGHIJKLMNOPQRSTU VWXYZ 1234567890 .,;:''«»&!?

Illus 24. An expanded typeface.

expansion board A component added to a computer system in order to enhance its capabilities. Expansion boards (also known as **add-on boards**) may provide the user with additional memory, graphics, colour, communications features, etc.

expose unit Also **exposure unit.** See **output scanner.**

exposure The process in which light sensitive materials (e.g. plates or film) are exposed to a light source.

extended nip press See **enp**.

extended type See **expanded type**.

extenders 1. Ink additives used to increase coverage. Typical extenders include whiting, borytes, blanc fixe. 2. **Ascenders** and **descenders** of a letter (q.v.).

extensible paper Paper which has tear-resistance due to stretching properties.

extent Length of a book in pages.

extract Quoted matter within a text, often set indented and in a smaller type size.

ex-warehouse Referring to a price quoted with no transport charges, as from the seller's own warehouse.

F

face 1. The printing surface of a piece of type. 2. A style of type, i.e. typeface.

face-down feed When the side of the sheet to be printed faces downward on the feed board.

facing Lining of fibreboard.

facing editorial Appearing opposite editorial pages. A special position used when ordering advertisement space.

facing pages Pages which face each other in an open book or magazine. Also **double-page spread**.

facsimile 1 Exact reproduction of a document or part of it. 2. Machine which copies and transmits documents by telecommunications. Hence **facsimile transmission**. Fax is divided into a number of groups, reflecting machine capabilities: groups 3 and 4 are the current standards. In group 3 fax, the document is scanned with a resolution typically of around 200dpi, compressed, and transmitted via a modem (if the **PSTN** is being used) or directly (if an **ISDN** can be used). At the receiving end the data is decompressed and reconstituted to the same 200dpi.

fade-out See **ghosting**.

fade-out halftone Alternative term for a **vignette** (q.v.).

fair copy A correction-free copy of a document.

fair dealing A provision in copyright law which permits the copying of an otherwise protected work for the purposes of criticism, review, or private study.

fake duotone Imitation duotone obtained by printing the half-tone in one colour (normally black) over a flat screen tint of another colour (lighter). Contrast **duotone** (q.v.).

fake process Colour separation achieved by means of the artist producing separate overlays.

family A series of **founts** related to the basic text roman face.

f&g sheets Folded and gathered sheets of a book.

fanfold A web of paper folded into connected sheets by alternate folds across the web.

fanning-in The condensing of the image on the trailing edge of a sheet caused by the sheet stretching temporarily on the press.

fan-out Moisture-distorted edges of paper on the press, creating waviness in the sheet.

fastback binding See **tightback binding**.

fastness Resistance of colour to fading. See also **lightfast ink, blue wool scale**.

fax Abbreviation for **facsimile transmission**.

FCL In seafreight, abbreviation for full container load. Compare **LCL**.

FDA regulations Food and Drug Administration's rules governing the use of packaging materials for food and drugs.

feathering 1. In printing, ink-spread on inadequately sized paper. 2. In typesetting, the addition of fractional parts of a point of leading between all lines in a page to "stretch" the text to a predefined depth. A form of **vertical justification** (q.v.).

featherweight paper Very bulky **antique** with low substance.

feature 1. Newspaper or magazine article. 2. Specially promoted item of merchandise or characteristic of that item.

feed board The surface over which paper is passed to the printing mechanism of a press.

feed edge Edge of a sheet presented to the lays of a press. Also called **gripper edge, leading edge**, or **pitch edge**.

feeder The mechanism on a press which separates and lifts sheets into the printing position. Feeders for printing machines fall into three broad types which are, in ascending order of capability: **friction feeders, single-sheet feeders, stream feeders**. Feeders for folding machines are of two main types: **round-pile feeders** and **flat-pile feeders**.

feed holes Holes in paper tape used by the sprocket on the mechanical reader to feed the tape in.

feed roller In a **dampening system** the roller which transfers the fountain solution from the **fountain roller** to the **distributor roller** for onward supply to the plate dampers; in an **inking system**, the roller which transfers ink from the **duct roller** to the **ink pyramid**, performing the

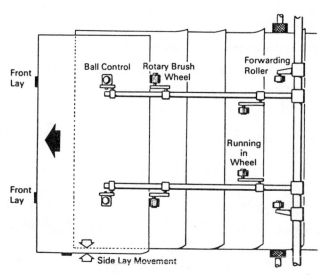

Illus 25. A typical feed board arrangement.

same service for the ink.

feet The base of a piece of metal type.

feint ruling Horizontal pale blue lines running across stationery.

felt finish A finish to paper created by felts with special weaves.

felt-side Top side of paper formed on a paper machine wire. As distinct from the **underside** or **wire side** (q.v.).

ferrous oxide Metallic coating on the surface of computer discs which can be locally magnetised in a series of spots whose positions are determined and tracked by the computer. The spots are applied and read by the **read-write head** in the disc drive of the computer. See also **disc**.

festoon In web-offset printing, an arrangement of long loops at the paper feed which allows paper to be tensioned during autopasting on the fly using a **flying paster** (q.v.).

fetch The process of getting the next instruction from memory.

ff Folios (plural).

fibre The raw material of papermaking: the **cellulose** and **hemicellulose** constituents in wood pulp which when separated from the **lignin** polymers which bind them in their natural state, become the main component in paper.

fibre cut Damage to the web on a paper-making machine caused by a bundle of fibres.

fibrefelt Another name for **imitation cloth** (q.v.).

fibre optic cable A protective glass or plastic cable containing a pure fibre of the same material, used to transmit light from **LEDs** or **lasers** in the communication of signals.

fibre optics The technique of communicating data by the transmission of light through plastic or glass fibres.

fibre puffing A roughening of the surface of mechanical or part-mechanical coated papers when printed and dried by heatset web offset.

fibrilla Part of cellulose fibre separated during the refining process.

fibrillation In paper-making, the process of roughening the outsides of the fibres to increase their bonding capabilities.

field A predefined area of a computer **record** (q.v.).

FIFO See **first in first out**.

figs Abbreviation for figures, the plural of **figure** (q.v.).

figure 1. A line illustration referred to in the text of a book. 2. A numeral, either in **Arabic** or **Roman** form (q.v.).

file Text, or any set of data held on a computer.

file conversion The process of changing either a file medium or its structure, usually required because of the introduction of new software or hardware.

file management An established procedure for the creation and maintenance of files.

file server System management computer in a **network** of computers. Typically holds database files which are accessible by all the computers on the network.

fill The use of the full width or **deckle** of a papermaking machine.

fill character A character, typically a space, that is added to a set of characters to make the set up to a given size.

filler advertisement Advertisement used to occupy redundant space rather than a booked insertion.

fillers Pigments added to the furnish of paper to improve the printing or opacity characteristics.

fill pattern A choice of patterns and shades used to fill objects created under most **wysiwyg** graphics packages. Originally a MacDraw/ MacPaint feature, now emulated by other software packages.

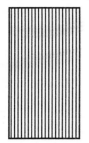  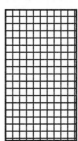

Illus 26. Some basic fill patterns.

film advance The distance by which film in a photosetter advances between lines of type to create **leading**. Also called **film feed** or **line feed**.

film feed See **film advance**.

filmless proofing or **filmless hardcopy proofing** Proofs generated off an electronic page composition system through the medium of, for example, a thermal colour printer. As distinct from **plastic proofs** (q.v.) which are made by contacting films or **machine proofs** which are made from plates.

film make-up Positioning pieces of film ready for platemaking. **Page make-up** is used as the term for pages or **assembly** for full imposition.

film master See **image master**.

film mechanical Camera-ready material composed in film rather than paper.

film plotter See **output scanner**.

film processor Machine which automatically develops, fixes, washes and dries exposed film.

film recorder See **output scanner**.

filmsetting Creating type on film by means of a photosetting system.

film wrapping See **plastic wrapping**.

filter Coloured gelatin or glass sheet placed over a lens to eliminate specific colours reaching the film. Used to separate colours for process printing.

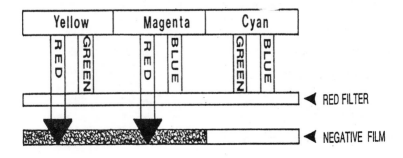

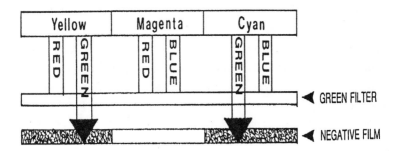

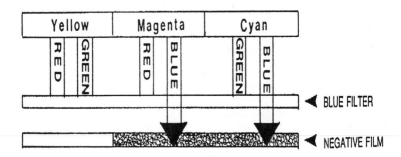

Illus 27. How filters are used to separate colours for process printing.

filter factor The extra exposure necessary to counteract the light-reducing effect of a filter.

finalisation The final preparation of plate-ready printing films, involving such operations as contacting to one-piece films, spotting out, etc.

Finder Apple Macintosh operating system.

fine etching Dot etching on metal plates to improve tone values.

fine grain Photographic paper with emulsion characteristics which are not obtrusive through the picture.

fine papers High quality printing and writing papers.

fines Small fragments of fibre remaining after refining.

fine screen A screen with ruling over 120 lines to the inch.

fingerprint A method of software protection in which a unique signature is written to a floppy disc. When the program is run, a test sequence checks for the presence of the signature and disables the program if it is found to be absent.

finish The type of surface on a particular grade of paper, e.g. **machine finished** or **supercalendered**. Also, **varnish** or **lamination** on a cover or jacket.

finishing Bindery processes taking place after a job is printed and bringing it to its final form ready for despatch, i.e. folding, stitching, cutting, inserting, etc.

FIPP International Federation of the Periodical Press.

firmware Software which is necessary for the general routines of a computer and which cannot be changed by the user. Usually held in **ROM** (q.v.).

first and second linings The two linings applied to the back of the book in case binding. The first lining is normally **mull**, a form of muslin cloth, the second lining normally **kraft**, a strong form of brown paper.

first and third Printed sheet which contains pages one and three after folding. See **outer forme**.

first colour down The first colour printed on a sheet when more than one colour is being used.

first-generation computers Early computers that used vacuum tubes.

first-generation photosetters Early photosetters modelled after hot metal machines and largely mechanical in operation.

first in first out (FIFO) Data storage method in which the first item recorded is the first to be retrieved.

first-level heading First (and most important) level in a series of headings in a book.

first proof The earliest proof used for checking by proof readers.

first revise The corrected proof made after errors noted on the first proof have been re-set.

fist Symbol of a hand with a pointing finger used to direct the reader to a certain part of the text.

fit Space between letters which can be reduced or expanded. See **character compensation, character fit, kerning.**

five-cylinder layout press See **common-impression press.**

fix Use chemicals to give permanency to a photographic image after development.

fixative Protective spray used on surface of artwork.

fixed back Book back glued directly to the back of the pages. Also **fastback, tightback binding.**

fixed length record In databases, a **record** that is of the same length as others with which it is associated.

fixed position Set location for an advertisement within a periodical, often specified by reference to other material, e.g. facing leader page.

fixed space The amount of space between letters and words which cannot be varied for justification needs. Contrast **variable space** (q.v.).

These words are separated by thin spaces.
These words are separated by en spaces.
These words are separated by em spaces.

Illus 28. Examples of fixed spaces.

flag 1. See **masthead.** 2. In text setting, a marker or reference mark inserted either to denote the word(s) marked for **database** purposes, or with the aim of compiling an index listing.

flap Protective cover for piece of artwork.

flash exposure Additional exposure given to a half-tone to enhance shadow areas.

flat 1. Lacking contrast when printed. 2. Assembled film on a carrier sheet ready for printing. Also **foil** (q.v.).

flat artwork Artwork which is drawn on a solid base and which cannot always be directly scanned.

flat back Bound with a flat back (as distinct from **rounded**). Also, **squareback**.

flatbed A press with the printing surface flat rather than curved as on a rotary press.

flatbed proofing press A litho flatbed press designed for producing machine proofs from colour separation plates in limited numbers.

flatbed scanner A scanner with a flat platen, rather like a photocopier, as opposed to one with a scanning drum. Also called **digital camera**.

flat etching Etching of a plate in a tray of solution.

flat-pile feeder Feeder which works from a flat as opposed to a round pile. One of the two main sorts of feeder used for folding machines. Compare **round-pile feeder**.

flat plan Diagrammatic scheme of the pagination of a magazine or book. Indicates available colour positions, so that colour illustrations can be positioned for printing in the most economical way.

flat tint plate Letterpress block used for printing a tint.

flat wrapping Wrapping a magazine with film or paper without folding it.

flax tow Linen fibres used in papermaking.

fleuron Typographical flower ornament used for decorative purposes. Known as a **dingbat** in DTP.

Illus 29. A fleuron.

flexiback binding Binding with reinforced spine using paper or fabric lining.

flexstabil binding Binding method used for heavy books and catalogues. A centre portion of the back of the book is scooped out, flooded with glue, and resealed, prior to the cover being drawn on. Extremely durable adhesive binding method.

flicker rate The rate at which a screen or monitor flickers, measured in **hertz**. A flicker rate of lower frequency than 50Hz is said to irritate the eye and lead to fatigue.

flier Promotional leaflet or handbill.

flimsy A carbon copy or other copy on thin bank paper.

flippy disc Double-sided **floppy disc** (q.v.).

float Centre a piece of artwork in an area which is too large for it.

floating accents Accents which are not tied to a given character in type fount and can therefore be positioned over any letter.

flocculation Ink-mixing fault caused when pigment floats as particles in the ink vehicle rather than dispersing smoothly. Solid areas have a spotty, pimply, appearance.

flong The special paper used for making moulds in stereotyping.

flooding Excess of ink on a printing plate.

flop Reverse film so that a mirror-image is produced.

floppy disc Small flexible plastic disc widely used for magnetic storage of information on micro computers. The standard size is 5.25 inches. **Microfloppy discs** are 3.5 inches.

floppy disc drive A device into which a floppy disc may be loaded and from which data may be read or written.

flotation de-inking Removing ink from recycled paper by creating a 'froth' which can be skimmed off.

flow The spread of ink over press rollers.

flowchart Diagram showing the sequence of steps in a computer program.

flowing In desktop publishing, the entering of text into a pre-formatted page such that it continues to fill out columns and/or pages until a rule or image is encountered, or until the text is exhausted.

fluff Loose surface fibres on paper. Also, **lint**.

fluffing The shedding of individual loose surface fibres from the surface of a paper on to a litho printing blanket causing a severe loss in printing quality. Fluffing is a risk with unsurface-sized papers printed by sheetfed offset litho. Also called **linting** or **piling**.

fluorescent ink Ink with extreme brightness qualities which react to ultra violet light. **Fluorescent papers** have fluorescent pigments added. Fluorescent whitening is included in pulp to add brightness to paper.

flush cover A cover trimmed flush with the pages of the text of the book.

flush left/right Type aligned with either the left or right-hand margins.

This line is flush left.

This line is centred.

This line is flush right.

Illus 30. Lines of type set flush left and flush right.

flush mount A letterpress plate mounted on its base with adhesive.

flying paster Pasting mechanism which joins a new reel of paper to that currently running out on a web press without stopping the press.

flying spot Light source used to scan documents in OCR machines.

flyleaf Blank leaf at the start of a book, usually pages 3-4 of the front **endpaper** (q.v.).

F number Defines the aperture of a lens at different settings, and is obtained by dividing the focal length of the lens by the diameter of the aperture. Also referred to as **f-stop**.

FOB Free on board. Carriage paid only up to the point of placing goods on board a vessel at the departure port. Contrast **CIF** (q.v.) which includes carriage payment right up to the specified delivery point.

FOC Father of Chapel. Print union equivalent of shop steward.

focal length The focal length of a lens is the distance between the lens and the film plane when rays from a distant object are in focus.

focal plane The plane where light entering a lens forms a sharp image.

focus Sharpness of definition in photography or in projection of a product or service.

fog Unintended light penetration of photographic materials.

foil 1. Carrier for planned films 2. In bookbinding, short for **stamping foil**: a plastic film coated with clear or coloured lacquer and a thin layer of condensed aluminium, which is used to block covers. The aluminium layer and coloured lacquer on top of it detach from the plastic carrier under heat and pressure from a **blocking brass** during the blocking process, leaving the design or lettering engraved on the block transferred into the surface of the case material with the thin coloured metallic layer on top of it. Popular colours are '**imitation gold**' and '**imitation silver**'.

foiling Another name for **blocking** (q.v.).

foil papers Papers with metallic surface.

folder Designation for a **file** or **directory** in the Apple Macintosh operating program.

folding boxboard High-quality carton maker's board which has good scoring and folding characteristics.

folding chases Chases which join to form a complete signature.

folding endurance Measure of deterioration of paper along a constantly repeated fold.

fold-out Folded sheet in text which opens out beyond the page size. Also, **gatefold, throw-out**.

foliation The numbering of manuscript pages.

folio 1. Page number at the head or foot of a page of text. 2. Sheet of copy. 3. Traditional term for an extra-large book format size, being half the size of a **broadside** sheet of paper.

folio cutter or **folio sheeter** Term applied to a cutter for large sheet sizes, as distinct from a cutter for the smaller **cut sizes** of paper.

folio sizes Printing sheet sizes, as distinct from small **cut sizes** (A4, etc.).

follow style Instruction to compositor to conform to the publisher's specified style.

font American spelling of **fount** (q.v.).

foolscap Paper size measuring $13\frac{1}{2}$ x 17 inches.

foot Bottom of a book or page.

foot margin The white margin at the foot of a book between the last line of text (or the foot folio) and the trimmed bottom of the page.

footnotes Notes explanatory to the main text, set in smaller type at the bottom of the page. Contrast **endnotes**.

footprint The surface area of a desk or bench that is required by an item of computer hardware.

force card Male die used in die-stamping.

fore-edge Outer edge of a book, opposite the binding edge.

fore-edge margin The outer margin in a book between the outer edge of each page and the outer edge of the type.

foreign rights The **subsidiary rights** in a published work which confer on a foreign publisher the right to translate and issue the work in his own language.

foreword Introduction to a book, not written by the author. As distinct from a **preface** (q.v.).

format 1. Trimmed page size, or physical specification for a page or a book. 2. Frequently occurring set of typographical commands stored as a code on a phototypesetter. 3. Structure imposed on a floppy disc by an operating system utility before it can be used to accept data. Also called **initialisation** (q.v.).

formation The fibre distribution of a sheet of paper. The two extremes are described as 'wild' or 'even'.

forme The printing surface as imposed and mounted ready for printing. By extension, a **flat** of pages imposed for printing one side of a sheet.

former folder Type of web press folder which draws paper over a **kite** (q.v.) to make first fold. As distinct from a **ribbon folder** (q.v.).

forme rollers Rollers in contact with the plate on a press.

forwarding Binding stages from after sewing until casing-in.

forwarding agent See **freight forwarder**.

forward slash A 45 degree rising slash, '/'. Also known as a **solidus** or **oblique**.

foul proofs Previous marked proofs.

foundry chase Chase used in stereo making.

foundry lockup A forme locked up for making moulds of electrotypes, stereotypes, etc.

foundry type Hard-wearing metal type characters used in hand composition.

fount A complete set of sorts all of the same typeface and point size.

fountain (also **fount**) Duct or trough on a printing press. The term normally indicates the water reservoir which holds the **dampening solution**, from which the **damping rollers** measure out the solution to the plate. As **ink fountain** (q.v.), the term is also used to indicate the ink duct.

fountain solution (also **fount solution**) Solution of water and chemicals used in litho to prevent the non-printing areas from accepting ink. Also, **dampening solution**.

four-colour process Colour printing with the three subtractive primary colours (yellow, magenta, cyan) plus black. The colours are separated photographically or by scanning.

Fourdrinier Paper-making machine named after the brothers who invented it. Uses a wire belt to convey the wet paper.

fourth cover Outside back cover of a periodical.

fourth-generation computers Computers using **LSI** – large scale integration – technology.

fourth-generation photosetters Photosetters using lasers to expose the characters.

fourth wave Used to describe typesetting and origination systems based on standard hardware and software, and with a high degree of compatibility with other systems and components.

franco domicile Referring to a price for a consignment which is delivered to the buyer's address with all arrangements made and costs paid by the seller.

free sheet 1. Periodical or newspaper distributed free to its readers. 2. **Woodfree paper** (U.S.) (q.v.).

freight forwarding The organisation of freight handling for customers. A **freight forwarder** can offer a variety of services, ranging from a comprehensive service including packing, full documentation, customs clearance, pick up and delivery of all his customer's freight, to a specialised service offering any part of the freight operation, eg customs clearance of a package at an airport.

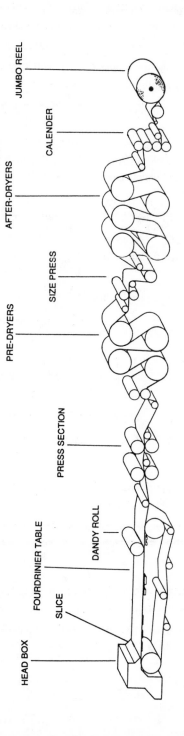

Illus 31. A Fourdrinier paper making machine.

French fold The fold used on Christmas cards, which folds a sheet into four visible printed pages, exposing only one side of the sheet and leaving the join at the top edge.

French groove In binding, the groove or channel left by bringing the case board slightly away from the shoulder of the book. Also, **joint**.

French sewing Plain, conventional sewing. Also called **section sewing** (q.v.).

frequency 1. How often a periodical is published (e.g. weekly, monthly, etc). 2. Number of times an advertisement is repeated. 3. Measurement of repetition of sound waves per second.

friction feeder Type of feeder associated with small offset printing machines in which each sheet is combed forward individually using a friction wheel.

friction glazing Form of glossy finish imparted to paper by a special calender.

frisket Device on a hand-press for holding down paper during printing.

front board The front cover or case of a book as opposed to its **back board** and **spine**.

front end General term for all the parts of a photosetting system before the output unit/imagesetter, e.g. input keyboards, screens, editing terminals, etc.

frontispiece Illustration on the page facing the title page of a book.

front-list A publisher's list of new and current titles.

frontmatter Prelims of a book.

front of book Part of a periodical before the bulk of the editorial pages, often dedicated to advertisements.

froth holes Small round craters in the surface of a coated paper caused by bubbles in the coating mix which burst as the coating is applied.

f stop See **F number**.

fugitive inks Inks which fade or change colour in unstable atmospheric conditions or in bright light.

fullbound Binding style in which the case covering material is one piece of cloth or leather. As distinct from **quarter-bound**, **half-bound**, or three-quarter bound.

full capitals or **full caps** Full-sized, regular capitals as distinct from **small capitals**.

full colour Four-colour process.

full duplex Data transmission in both directions simultaneously. Contrast **simplex, half duplex**.

full-faced capitals or **full-faced caps** See **full capitals**.

full measure Complete width of a column of text.

full-out Set flush with no indentations.

full point Full stop.

full run All the editions of a newspaper.

function codes Codes which control the function of a phototypesetter or output device rather than generating characters.

function keys Keys on a computer labelled F1 to F10 which carry out specific functions when pressed.

furnish The components in a paper.

furniture Letterpress spacing material.

fuzz Loosely bonded fibres projecting from the surface of paper.

FWA Fluorescent Whitening Agent. A loading similar to an **OBA** (q.v.) added to paper to increase whiteness and brightness.

G

gallery The camera department in a process engraving house.

galley proof Proof of typematter not made up into page. Also known as **slip proof**.

galvanised Inconsistent in colour or density of printed ink.

gamma A measure of contrast in photographic processing.

gang printing Running more than one job on the same sheet.

gap 1. The space between records on disc or tape. 2. The space between a read/write head and the recording medium.

Garalde Category of typeface also known as **Old Face** and taking in most of the classic book designs such as Bembo, Garamond, Plantin.

garbage Redundant programs or data.

gas plasma display An alternative to the cathode ray tube in a **VDU**, a gas plasma display consists of a sealed unit made from two sheets of flat glass filled with a neon/argon gas. Conductors are etched on to the glass plates (vertical on the front plate, horizontal on the rear plate) and images are formed when currents coincide at conductor junctions.

gate Part of a computer circuit which tests a precondition in a program, e.g. the statements 'and' and 'or'.

gatefold A page in a magazine or book which folds out to double its size.

gateway Equipment designed to interface **networks** so that a terminal in one network may communicate with a device that is part of another network.

GATF Graphic Arts Technical Foundation, Pittsburg, U.S.A.

gathering Collecting sheets or signatures of a printed job into the correct sequence for binding. See also **collate**.

Gb Abbreviation for gigabyte (q.v.).

gcc See **calcium carbonate**.

GCR See **grey component replacement**.

gear streaks Marks on a printed sheet caused by the gears on a press cylinder.

GEM In computing, a **graphical user interface** rather similar to Microsoft Windows or the AppleMac interface which uses pictures and icons. The abbreviations stand for Graphical Environment Manager. See the **WIMP** concept.

generation 1. Stage of reproduction from an original.2. Stage of development of a technology, e.g. fourth-generation phototypesetters.

generic coding Strictly speaking, coding the structure of a document rather than its typographical constituents. But often used to include generalised typographic coding or 'tagging' of the **ASPIC** variety − headings marked h1, h2, etc − which are applied to indicate typographic levels of heading for later conversion to typesetting codes. Also, **generic mark-up**.

generic face or **generic fount** A fount used in screen display or as output for a laser proofer to represent an entire category of higher-quality output founts. To ensure that line endings in the generic fount match the eventual output, inter-character spacing is adjusted to compensate for the variations in set width between the generic fount and the ultimate output fount.

generic mark-up The allocation of tags to headings which identify common features for database or typesetting purposes. See **generic coding**.

generic tags Simple codes − A,B,C, etc, or h1, h2, h3 − which can be used to identify levels of heading or text setting for later conversion to typography.

Geometrics A category of **Lineale** (sans serif) typefaces whose character forms are based on simple geometric shapes such as circles or rectangles. Examples include Erbar, Eurostile, Futura.

abcdefghijklmnopqrstuvwxyz
ABCDEFGHIJKLMNOPQRSTUVWXYZ
1234567890 .,;:"«»&!?

Illus 32. Futura, an example of a Geometric typeface.

ghosting A second lighter image which appears on the print as a ghost image. It is due either to the litho blanket having an engraved image from a previous run; or (more normally) by the print on the reverse side of the sheet affecting the trapping and drying of the new ink leaving a faint image of reduced gloss as a ghost. Not to be confused with a **repeat** (q.v.) which is typically caused by ink starvation on the press.

gigabyte Gb One thousand million **bytes** (q.v.). One gigabyte of computer storage is roughly equivalent to 150 million words of text, or the text content of 2000 average-sized novels.

1 Gb	150 million words	330,000 A4s
5 Gb	750 million words	1,650,000 A4s
10 Gb	1500 million words	3,300,000 A4s

gigo Garbage in, garbage out. Programmer's slang to describe bad output caused by faulty data.

gilt in the round Foredge of a book gilded after the book has been rounded. Achieves better cover than **gilt in the square**: gilded before rounding.

give-away Free promotional leaflet or gift.

glair Substance which bonds gold leaf to leather.

glassine Tough but partially transparent paper used for protective purposes, for plain jacket wrappers and for overlays on artwork.

glazed In paper, refers to a lightly supercalendered finish, somewhere in appearance between an MF printing and a more regular supercalendered 'gloss'.

glazed vellum Vellum paper with a glazed surface, used for decorative documents.

global search and replace The facility of a computer program to find all examples of a word or group of words in a file and replace them with an alternative.

gloss art Shiny artpaper as opposed to **matt art** or **coated cartridge** papers which have a dull finish.

glossary Alphabetically arranged list of terms and their meanings.

glossy Photographic print with a glossy surface.

glueability Measure of speed of paper adhesive bonding and its strength.

Glyphics Typefaces based on chiselled rather than calligraphic forms.

glytch Program error.

goldenrod paper Opaque orange paper on which film is assembled for platemaking.

gold foil Paper with a foil coating. **Gold leaf** comprises thin sheets of real gold.

golfball typewriter Typewriter using a replaceable spherical head, or 'golfball'. Each golfball represents one type face.

Gothics See **Grotesques**.

grade In paper, a sort or **quality** of paper: bulky mechanicals, woodfree coateds, etc, are different grades or qualities of paper.

grain direction Direction of fibres in a sheet of paper. **Long grain** describes fibres running parallel with the longest side of a sheet; **short grain** along the shortest side. Each time a sheet of paper is cut in two across its short dimension its grain direction changes. Grain direction is also known as **machine direction**.

graining 1. Mechanical roughening of a litho plate to retain water. 2. Treatment of paper, board, or laminated board to give a textured effect.

grainy Photographic film or print with coarse 'grain' visible usually due to high speed of film.

grainy edge Surface roughness on edges of web caused in the drying process.

grammage Weight of paper expressed as grams per square metre.

Graphic Category of typeface distinguished from the **Script** category by the appearance of having been drawn rather than handwritten.

graphical user interface User-friendly screen presentation employing pictures and icons. A **WIMP** environment (q.v.).

graphic papers Papers for printing or writing.

graphics Pictures and illustrations in printed work.

graphics display terminal A VDU capable of displaying pictures in line or tone in addition to text.

graphics insertion Text and pictures photoset in one operation.

graphics primitives Simple geometric shapes from which an infinity of greater shapes can be built up.

graphics tablet Calibrated tablet on which, using a **light pen** (q.v.), an operator brings together components of a design and fixes them electronically in their correct positions according to the required design or layout.

grater roller Roller on a web-offset press which carries the web. See also **air bar**.

gravure printing Process in which recesses on a cylinder are filled with ink and the surplus removed with a blade. The paper contacts the cylinder and 'lifts' the ink from the recesses. Used for long-run magazines and catalogues.

greaseproof Translucent paper with high resistance to grease penetration.

great primer Obsolete term for 18pt type.

grey balance The ability to print a neutral grey from four-colour printing plates with no coloured tinges showing through. Monitored by a grey balance patch on colour bars.

grey board or **Dutch grey board** Homogenous caseboard made from newsprint furnish. Grey board or **unlined chipboard** (q.v.) are the normal boards used for casemaking. **Millboard** (q.v.) is used for specific heavy-duty bindings e.g. stationery or archive bindings.

grey component replacement GCR Colour separations where the black printer carries more detail than with conventional separations and the tertiary, or complementary, elements of any colour hue are removed. Also called **ICR (integrated colour removal)** or **achromatic separation**.

grey level Separate tone of grey reflecting back from a continuous-tone original. The grey levels of a continuous tone original are commonly defined in terms of 16, 64 or 256 steps, going from pure white to pure black. In the case of 256 grey levels, each step is identified by a different 8-bit number from the range binary 00000000 (decimal 0 - complete black) to binary 11111111 (decimal 255 - complete white). In scanning an original, the grey level value of each **pixel** of the original is sampled by an **analyse scanner** and allocated its grey level value as one of these 256 steps.

grey scale Strip of grey tones from white to black, used to measure tonal range against a standard.

grey scale value Alternative term for grey level.

grid 1. Sheet with ruled lines used to ensure square make-up of photocomposed material. 2. Systematic division of a page into type areas and positions for other regularly occurring features (headline, folios etc.) Sometimes printed in drop-out blue and used for camera-paste-up purposes.

grip Margins needed at the feed edge of a sheet of paper for the grippers on the press. Also **gripper edge** and **gripper margin.**

gripper Device on a printing press for holding the sheet.

gross profit In book publishing terms, the difference between the sales revenues of a book and the direct costs laid out to obtain those sales, ie net revenue less production costs, royalties, direct promotion costs. Contrast **net profit.**

Grotesques Early designs of sans serif typeface from the first decades of the nineteenth century, such as Grot 215. Also, **Gothics.**

abcdefghijklmnopqrstuvwxyz
ABCDEFGHIJKLMNOPQRSTUVWXYZ
1234567890 .,;:"«»&!?

Illus 33. Grot 215, an example of a Grotesque typeface.

ground US terminology for electrical earth.

groundwood pulp American term for **mechanical pulp.**

groundwood sheet Paper containing mainly **mechanical pulp** (US).

gsm Grams per square metre: the measure of **substance** of paper or board.

guard Linen or paper put on the back of a book section to provide additional strength. The process of doing this is known as **guarding** a section. The first and last sections of a heavy reference work may be guarded in this way.

guide Device on a printing press which locates sheets in position. The **guide edge** of a sheet is that which is fed up to the guide. Also, **lay.**

guideline Line on artwork indicating the printing area. Also, **keyline.**

guillemets Angled quotation marks, used in French.

guillotine Machine which cuts paper into sheets. **Programmatic guillotines** can perform a whole series of measured cuts without re-setting for each measurement.

gum arabic A hydrophilic vegetable gum used in fountain solutions, plate gum solutions and desensitising plate etch solutions.

gummed paper Paper coated on one side with adhesive.

gumming Applying adhesive to paper.

gum up To apply gum arabic to a litho plate and dry it off for storage. Gum arabic protects the image area and prevents **oxidation**.

gun The component of a cathode ray tube that provides a continuous stream of electrons. A monochrome display will require a single gun while colour displays must be provided with three, one each for red, green and blue.

gusseting Waving occurring at the heads of untrimmed signatures.

gutter Binding margin of a book.

GW Abbreviation for **groundwood pulp**.

H

H Abbreviation for horizontal.

hache The symbol '#' used to mean 'number', or as a proof-reading mark to mean space.

hair cut Curved cut in a web on a paper-making machine.

hairline Very fine line or stroke in a letter. **Hairline register** is colour register within + or - half a row of dots.

hair spaces Very thin letterpress spaces used between letters in a word.

halation Blurred halo effect in the highlight areas of a photo, caused by reflection back from the emulsion substrate.

half-bound Book case binding style: covered in one material on the spine and corners, and another material − paper or cloth − on the remainder.

half-duplex Data transmission in both directions but not at the same time. Contrast **simplex, full duplex**.

half page Advertisement occupying half a periodical page, horizontally or vertically.

half plate Photo measuring 6 x 4 inches.

half sheet work See **work and turn**.

half-size press Printing press designed for a maximum sheet approximately 710 x 1010 mm (28" x 40"), ie. half the size of a **quad** sheet. See also **mini-web**.

half title Title of book, sometimes shortened, printed on the first right-hand page in the book − the **half-title page**. Sometimes called **bastard title**.

half-tone Illustration created by dots of varying size, and giving the illusion of 'continuous tone'. Therefore, **half-tone negative** and **half-tone positive**.

half-tone screen Cross-ruled film or glass plate used to create half-tone dots. Dot formations can be round elliptical, rectangular, or pincushion.

half-up Instruction to prepare artwork at 150% of final size.

halo The area of low density surrounding the dense core of a halftone dot.

halo effect Build-up of ink at edges of printed letters and half-tone dots, creating a darker perimeter to the dot.

handbill Publicity sheet, normally printed on one side only, for delivery by hand.

handling stiffness Rigidity of paper when held, e.g. stiffness of a newspaper held by the reader.

h&j Hyphenation and justification.

hand-made paper Paper made by hand in a mould. Decorative content can be introduced into the pulp. The edges are **deckled** (q.v.).

handout Publicity leaflet for handing out on the street, at exhibitions, etc.

hand setting Making up lines of metal type by hand, usually in a composing 'stick'.

handshake A data communications technique consisting or prearranged signals which monitor the transmission of data by halting and restarting the flow as necessary and ensuring the integrity of the whole.

hanging indent Typesetting style in which the first line of a paragraph is set full out and the remainder are indented. Also **hanging pars** or **hanging paragraphs**, text set in this way.

hanging punctuation Punctuation marks at the end of justified lines which are allowed to jut out very slightly in order to give a visually straight right-hand edge to a column or page. Effect achievable only on sophisticated hyphenation and justification programs.

hardback or **hard-bound** See **case-bound**.

hard copy Copy written, typed or printed as distinct from stored in electronic form.

hardcover See **case-bound**.

hard disc A rigid magnetic storage disc capable of higher data density and speed than floppy discs. See **floppy disc, Winchester disc**.

hard-dot positives Film produced either by contact or by direct laser scanning where the dot edges are hard and can be retouched by hand only to a limited extent.

hard fount In laser printers, a fount which is provided as a plug-in cartridge. As distinct from a **resident (internal) fount**; or a **soft fount** (q.v.).

hard hyphen Hyphen essential to the spelling of a word. Contrast **soft hyphen** (q.v.) or **discretionary hyphen**.

hardness Resistance of paper to indentation by printing plate, type or pen.

hard RAM An allocation of **RAM** available in some microcomputers which is independently powered by a small battery, and which therefore retains its contents after the computer is switched off. Also, **RAM cache**.

hard-sectored Describing floppy discs physically divided into sectors by means of index holes in the disc surface. Compare **soft-sectored**.

hard-sized Paper with a high degree of internal and external **sizing** (q.v.).

hardware Computer term for equipment as distinct from programs.

hard-wired Circuit or program as constructed by the manufacturer of a piece of hardware and which cannot be changed.

hardwood pulp Pulp made from hardwood (deciduous) trees, e.g. oak, beech, birch, eucalyptus. As distinct from **softwood pulp** (q.v.).

harlequin Ornamented typographical character.

Harvard system System of bibliographical references which originated in Harvard University.

hatch Draw closely spaced lines in a drawing to give the effect of tone.

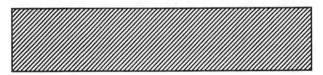

Illus 34. An example of hatching.

HD Abbreviation for 1. hard disc, or 2. high density (referring to a disc's formatting capacity).

head 1. Top or top margin of a page. 2. **Heading** (q.v.). 3. The part of a **disc drive** which reads and writes magnetic information from and to a computer disc.

headband Cotton or silk cord attached to the top of the back of a book. Headbands can have either string centres, or more expensively but durably, cane centres. See also **tailband**.

headbox The part of a paper-making machine which dispenses the **stock**

on the moving wire.

header That part of a message about a collection of data which gives information about the data itself.

heading 1. Title of a section or chapter in a work, set in displayed type. 2. See **headline**.

headline A displayed line or lines at the top of a page or a piece of text. See also **running head.**

headliner Phototypesetting machine designed to produce lines of display-sized type.

head margin The white space between the first line of text on a page and the trimmed head of the page.

heads In imposition, the **head margins** (q.v.).

head-to-head, head-to-tail Alternative imposition schemes for a pair of books or printed covers/jackets which are printed as one and cut apart at the final stage.

headword Word beginning a reference in a dictionary or directory. Often set in bold type.

heat-resistant splice Join in paper which will resist the heat of a heat-set press.

heat sealing Closing plastic bags by semi-melting techniques.

heat seal paper Paper coated on one side with adhesive activated by heat.

heat-set Drying of ink on paper using heat, on a web-offset machine. Hence **heat-set inks.**

heat sink Material employed to conduct heat away from a component.

heat transfer Transfer of ink from paper to another material (e.g. fabric) by heat and pressure. Special paper and ink are necessary.

Heidelberg 1. Heidelberg Druckmaschinen AG, West German manufacturer of printing machinery sold world wide. 2. Proprietary name for the range of printing machines made by this manufacturer.

height to paper Standard height of letterpress type and blocks. Varies from country to country.

helium-neon laser setter Laser setter in which the imaging method is by continuous helium-neon laser beam as distinct from the alternative technology of **laser diode** imaging.

hemicellulose Fibrous compound similar to cellulose and found in plant life. A constituent in papermaking **fibre** (q.v.).

Hempel quoins Expandable wedges used to lock up letterpress formes.

hemp fibre Papermaking fibre made from rope or from the hemp plant.

Hermes UK teletext and electronic mail system.

hertz A frequency unit equivalent to one unit or cycle per second. In the case of computers, processing speed is reckoned in megahertz (**MHz**). Most micros are rated between 5 MHz at the lower end, up to 20MHz at the top.

hexadecimal Also, **hex** A numeric notation scheme with a base of 16. In hex, decimals 0-15 become 00, 01, 02, 03, 04, 05, 06 07, 08, 09, 0A, 0B, 0C, 0D, 0E, OF. Decimal 16 is then 10; decimal 17 is 11; decimal 27 is 1B; and so on.

hickey Solid spot with a halo round it which shows on a printed sheet as a blemish. Caused by dust, lint or ink imperfectionsm and particularly noticeable in solids, large type half-tones, tints, etc. Also known as **doughnut.**

high density plastic Thin, strong plastic film used for wrapping magazines where weight is critical.

high key Tonal values lighter than mid-grey.

high-level language A computer programming language which uses English-language instructions. Use of a high-level language then requires a translator program within the computer to convert these instructions from high-level language into **machine-code**. See also **low-level language**.

highlights Lightest tonal values in a half-tone representing tonal values of 0% - 30%. Contrast **mid-tones, shadows**.

high spaces Letterpress spaces cast to shoulder height of type and used in formes for stereotyping.

high speed Data communications speeds above 9600 bits per second, being in excess of speeds normally attainable via voice-grade circuitry.

high-speed dataline A closed circuit transmission line capable of supporting very high data transmission speeds.

high-yield pulp Synonym for **CTMP**, or **chemi-thermomechanical pulp** (q.v.).

hints Adobe's PostScript programming techniques enabling the efficient and accurate outlining of low-resolution versions of PostScript founts.

hold Retain matter for subsequent use.

holding fee Also called a **blocking fee**. The fee charged by a picture library when a picture is retained by a client beyond the agreed period.

holding lines Design lines which indicate the area of a piece of artwork on a page (US).

holdout Resistance to ink absorption of a paper.

hollorap carton See **buffered carton**.

hollow 1. Space between the case and the back of the sewn sections in a hardbound book. 2. By extension, the material used for reinforcing the inside spine of a case. Examples include a **board hollow, presspahn hollow, paper hollow, oxford hollow**.

hologram, holograph A three-dimensional image created by lasers.

homogenous A homogenous board is made on a Fourdinier machine of one furnish throughout. A **pasteboard** (q.v.) is made up of two or more plys of different papers or homogenous boards which are pasted together.

Honda interface Traditional method of data transmission from publisher to supplier and vice versa. Reliability sometimes affected by rainfall.

hooked An illustration or plate can be hooked in a book by folding the paper along the edge and wrapping the edge round the outside of a section. The illustration/plate is then secured with that section in the binding.

hopper Station on a machine (especially in binding) where printed sections are stacked and dropped on to a conveyer belt.

hopsack One of a variety of finishes typically offered in **imitation cloth**. Hopsack is a coarse-weave finish.

host 1. Main central processing unit in a multi-computer system. 2. Holder of an online database.

hotmelt Type of synthetic resin adhesive used in perfect binding. Can be used alone (**one-shot binding**) or in conjunction with **PVA** (**two-shot**

binding). Hotmelt glue is solid at room temperature, and is applied at high temperature. It has high initial tack, dries quickly, but is rather less flexible than **PVA**.

house advertisement A filler advertisement (q.v.) for a periodical's own company.

house copies Copies of a magazine for use within the publishing house rather than for sale.

house corrections Errors introduced by the typesetter and either corrected before proofs are sent to the customer, or marked on the customer's proofs for his attention.

housekeeping File initialisation, creation, maintenance and back-up tasks.

house style See **style of the house**.

HSWO Heatset web-offset.

hue Perceivable quality of a colour - e.g. redness or blueness - which distinguishes it from other colours. As distinct from its **shade** (lightness or darkness).

Humanist Category of typeface based on the earliest roman letterforms. Also known as **Venetian**. Examples include Centaur, Horley Old Style, Kennerley.

abcdefghijklmnopqrstuvwxyz
ABCDEFGHIJKLMNOPQRSTUVW
XYZ 1234567890 .,;:"&!?

Illus 35. Horley Old Style, an example of a Humanist typeface.

humidification Addition of water vapour to air.

humidity Quantity of water vapour in the atmosphere. See also **absolute humidity** and **relative humidity**.

Hunter Lab values American scales, used to measure colour.

HWC Heavyweight coated. Mechanical coated paper of around 85gsm and above. Compare, **ULWC**, **LWC**, **MWC**.

hybrid computer One which has elements of both digital and analogue computers.

hydrapulper Large circular metal tank in which dry pulp is mixed with water, and other ingredients added, in the first stages of papermaking (**breaking**). The stock from the hydrapulper passes on for **refining** (q.v.) in a **cone refiner** system prior to release to the paper machine.

hydrophilic Water-attracting.

hydrophobic Water-repelling.

hygro-expansivity Growth or shrinkage of paper due to moisture content. Hence also **hygro-instability**.

hygrometer Instrument used to measure relative humidity.

hygrometry Measurement of humidity.

hygroscopic Absorbing moisture.

hyphen Short horizontal rule to indicate the connection in a compound word, or to divide a word at the end of a justified line in typesetting. Unlike the case in typewriting, a hyphen is distinct from an en or an em rule in typography, being around half the length of an en rule, and rather thicker in stroke.

hyphenation The division of words, in word processing and desktop publishing, which will not fit on the current line. Hyphenation is achieved either by accessing a dictionary or by reference to a table of logical rules.

hyphenation exception dictionary In word processing and typesetting, a dictionary of words, held in computer memory, which if hyphenated by the normal rules of hyphenation logic may break at an unacceptable point. When the typesetting computer needs to break a word at the end of a sentence, it will first refer to its hypenation exception dictionary to see if the word is there, and if so, will break it at one of the **discretionary hyphen points** allotted to the word. If the word is not in the dictionary, it will break it according to the rules of logic programmed in it.

hyphenation logic Programming to break words according to logical rules. The so-called **3-5-7 rule** is the first if very primitive rule of logic which may be applied to obtain basic English language hyphenation: words are broken after the third, fifth or seventh letter. Further refinements in a logic program may include the identification of common prefixes and suffixes so that words can be broken at these points; and the identification of other common letter-groups which provide logical break-points.

hyphenless justification Justification without breaking words. On narrow measures this creates widely varying spacing characteristics.

> This is an example of hyphenless justification across a narrow measure. You will observe that this creates unacceptable variations in spacing between the words.

Illus 36. Hyphenless justification.

hypo Abbreviation for sodium hyposulphite, a chemical used to fix photographic images after development.

I

IBC Inside back cover.

I-beam I-shaped cursor which appears on the screen in certain programs running on an Apple Macintosh computer, and which is normally used to define the position on the screen where text will be placed as it is typed in.

ibid Abbreviated Latin 'ibidem' meaning 'in the same place': used in reference books or citations to refer to the same article, etc, as previously mentioned.

IBM-compatible A term applied to personal computers which their manufacturers claim will accept hardware add-ons and run software designed to run on an IBM-PC.

IBM PC IBM microcomputer (personal computer).

icon A pictorial representation of an object or function in a computer display. For example, the function to file a record may be represented by a picture of a file or folder.

ICR 1. **Integrated colour removal** : see **achromatic separations**. 2. **Intelligent character recognition** (q.v.).

ICs Integrated circuits (q.v.).

idiot tape Unformatted tape with no line ending commands.

idle time Time on a machine when it is not in use for productive work.

IF In high-level programming a conditional statement in which action is taken only if the condition is met.

I/F Interface (q.v.).

illustration board One-sided heavy drawing card.

image Printing areas of a litho plate.

image area piling Build up of lint and ink on litho press blanket in the image area.

image master Photographic original for second-generation photosetting founts. Also, **film master**.

image plotter See **imagesetter**.

image recorder See **imagesetter**.

imagesetter Useful portmanteau term to describe any output device (but typically a laser recording unit) which can process and output text and graphics indiscriminately. Synonyms are **image plotter, image recorder, laser plotter, laser recorder, laser setter, laser output unit, film recorder,** etc.

imitation art Paper loaded with china clay in the pulp and highly finished to give an 'artpaper' appearance. As distinct from true **art paper,** which has a china clay surface applied to a conventional base paper.

imitation cloth Reinforced and embossed paper commonly used for binding hardback books instead of cotton cloth.Also, **fibrefelt.** Contrast **woven material.**

imitation gold foil Aluminium foil with gold lacquer on plastic carrier. Used for blocking the covers of books.

imitation leather PVC-coated paper grained to simulate leather and used for bookbinding.

imitation parchment Tough greaseproof paper.

imitation silver foil Aluminium foil with clear lacquer on plastic carrier. Used for blocking the covers of books.

impact printer Any printer in which the required character strikes the paper through an inked ribbon. See **daisywheel printer, dot matrix printer.**

imperfection Book with printing or binding faults.

imposed colour proofs Colour proofs produced from machine formes which are imposed to the final page sequence of the job. Contrast **scatter proofs.** The main advantage of imposed colour proofs is that the effects of **tracking** (q.v.) can be properly considered.

imposed page proofs Page proofs either in **blueprint** form or pulled from the printing plates, imposed in book running order.

imposition Arrangement of pages in a sequence which will read consecutively when the printed sheet is folded. Hence **imposition scheme.**

impregnating Running book binding cloth through starches or chemicals to enhance its quality or appearance.

impression 1. Pressure of the plate in contact with paper or blanket at the moment of printing. 2. All the copies of a book from one printing.

impression cylinder Cylinder which holds the paper against the printing surface.

impression tolerance The flexibility with which paper receives letterpress impression.

imprimatur The official licence to print a book.

imprint Publisher's and/or printer's identifying text printed in a book or other work. The publisher's imprint traditionally appears on the title page, while the printer's imprint appears on the biblio page. See also **colophon**.

improved mechanical A mechanical printing paper improved by virtue of a somewhat superior furnish (perhaps **RMP** or **TMP**) and given a higher degree of bleaching and calendering than for normal **bulky news**.

inching In printing press make-ready, to move the cylinders round an inch at a time to facilitate plate registration, or washing up, etc.

inclusive type area Type area inclusive of headline and folio. Contrast exclusive type area (q.v.).

incunabula Early printing.

indent 1. Set type further in from the left-hand margin than the standard measure of surrounding text. 2. In paper trading, an **indent** paper is one which is available from the mill by special making order only, and is not held in common stock by the mill as a standard line.

index 1. Alphabetical list of subjects contained in the text of a work, together with their page numbers. 2. The contents of a file with references for locating the contents.

index board Board suitable for index cards and similar stationery.

index hole A hole in a floppy disc which is used to signal the start of a **track** or **sector**.

indexing In CRT typography, the undesirable effect of step-like outlines around a letter. Most apparent when large sizes of type are printed on smooth or coated papers. Also called **stepping**. The steps themselves are called **striations** (q.v.).

Indian ink Intensely black drawing ink.

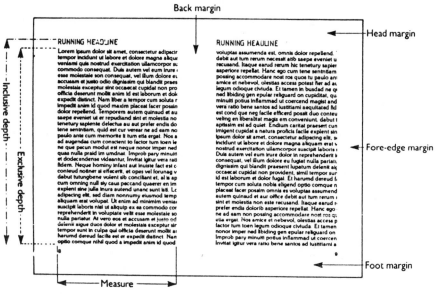

Illus 37. Inclusive and exclusive type areas.

india paper Very thin opaque rag paper often used for high quality bibles.

indicia Formal mailing information or permit printed on envelope or item to be mailed.

indirect letterpress See **letterset**.

indirect printing Process where the printing surface is not in direct contact with the paper, e.g. offset litho.

indirect screening Four-colour origination in which the final output films are in continuous tone, and are screened afterwards, separately, rather than as they are output from the scanner. Contrast **direct screening**.

infeed rollers Rollers on a web-offset press which draw the web forward off the reel stand.

inferior Small character set below the base line at the foot of another character. Also known as a **subscript**.

These$_1$ numbers$_2$ are$_3$ inferior$_4$ characters$_5$.

Illus 38. Inferior characters.

information retrieval Holding text in an electronic file so that it may be accessed by a computer.

ingrain paper Rough surfaced paper for book covers.

in-house typesetting Typesetting carried out inside a publisher's premises, and controlled by the publisher.

initial First letter in text when set in such a way that it stands out, e.g. bigger than its normal cap text size. See **cocked-up initial**, **drop initial**.

initialise In computing, to **format** a disc. This process, which prepares the locations on the disc for data to be stored, erases any existing data stored on the disc at the time that the 'initialise' command is carried out.

ink agitator Mechanical device fitted to the ink duct of a litho press which intermittently moves along its length stirring the ink. See **thixotropy**.

ink duct Part of printing machine which holds ink before it is released to the cylinders. Also, **ink fountain**.

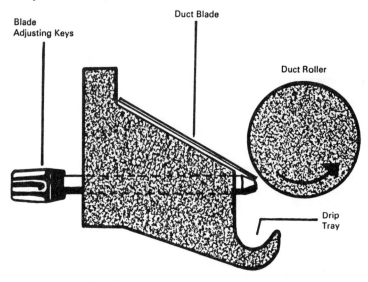

Illus 39. A conventional ink duct.

inker damping The principle of applying the dampening solution to a litho plate not directly but via the inking rollers. Examples include the Rotafount system and the Dahlgren inker damping system. Inks specially formulated to counteract **emulsification** are needed.

ink flotation sizing test Test which measures paper sizing by floating paper on ink and calculating penetration time.

ink fountain Trough which supplies ink to the inking rollers. Also **ink duct**.

ink hickey See hickey.

ink holdout See **holdout**.

inking system A typical inking system for a litho press starts with an ink reservoir or **duct**. Inside the duct revolves a **duct roller** which builds up a metered layer of ink on its surface. A **feed roller (vibrator roller)** makes intermittent contact with the duct roller to pick up a strip of ink and transfer it to the start of the **ink pyramid**. The pyramid consists of a large number of rollers of different diameters set in a pyramid shape which meter down the ink. A series of **reciprocating rollers** aid the levelling and evening-out process. Finally the ink reaches the **plate inkers** which distribute an even film of ink to the plate.

ink jet printer A **non-impact printing** mechanism which forms the image at high speed by deflecting ink droplets electromagnetically.

ink mist Ink filaments thrown off the rollers during high-speed cold-set web offset printing.

inkometer Instrument which measures the tack of ink.

ink piling Build-up of ink on offset blanket.

ink pyramid See under **inking system**.

ink receptivity Uniform acceptability of ink on paper surface.

ink rub Smears of ink caused when the surface of an abrasive paper, often **matt art**, rubs against the ink film before it is completely dry. Often occurs during the binding process.

ink set-off Unwanted transfer of wet ink from one printed sheet to another in the delivery stack.

ink starvation Ink starvation is caused by the image on one part of the plate cylinder requiring more ink to cover it than that particular **track** of the inking rollers can handle.

ink train Alternative term for ink pyramid. See **inking system**.

inlay carton Special packing carton which holds a book in a specially cut-out hollow tray inside an outer box.

inline Typographic style in which the characters comprise white inner areas contrasting against the outlined shape.

in-line press See **unit press**.

inner forme The imposed forme which forms the inside of the sheet when folded and which therefore contains the second page of the section. Contrast **outer forme**.

in pro In proportion. Also **RIP** (q.v.).

input Data going into a **CPU**.

insert Plate section placed into the middle of a text section in a book. Contrast **wrap**.

inserting Placing loose material inside a section or book.

insertion Inclusion of an advertisement in a periodical.

insetting Placing and fixing one section inside another.

inspection copy Copy of a book set to a potential customer (often a school) for inspection prior to buying.

instruction Order in a program telling a computer to carry out an operation.

intaglio Printing from a recessed image, e.g. gravure, die stamping, etc.

integrated book Book with text and pictures together throughout and all printed on the same paper (as opposed to pictures in a separate artpaper plate section).

integrated circuit Silicon chip.

integrated colour removal ICR See **achromatic separations**.

integrated half-tone density See **percentage dot area**.

intelligent character recognition ICR Optical character recognition techniques which are further enhanced by programming equipment to recognise an infinite variety of styles. This is distinct from straightforward OCR systems which will recognise only strictly limited ranges of typewriter face or typeface only.

intelligent terminal A microcomputer connected to a host computer. The device may operate as a stand-alone unit or as an element of a network.

interactive Computer system used in **real time** so that the operator can issue commands which affect the processing and simultaneously see the results of the commands. An **interactive page make-up program** is one where the operator sees the results of his instructions on the screen as soon as he makes them. Contrast **batch pagination program.**

intercharacter spacing In word processing, the use of variable spaces between characters which, in conjunction with variable interword spacing, combine to give an impression of typeset quality. Also, **letterspacing.**

interface The link between parts of a computer system, varying from a simple cable connection to an 'intelligent' device which translates protocol.

interfacing codes Generic tags used for the electronic mark-up of headings, etc, in text.

interlay (cut or mechanical) Cut-out paper placed between a letterpress plate and its mount which increases pressure on the solids or dark tones.

interleaves 1. Sheets of paper put between wet printed sheets to prevent set-off. 2. Different types of paper interleaved with the text paper in a book.

interlinespacing Leading: space between lines in text. Also, **film advance, film feed, line feed, leading.**

intermediates Films used in the intermediate stages of reproduction between the original and final printing films. Normally **continuous tone.**

internal fount In laser printers, a fount which is supplied resident in the printer's computer, and so always available. As distinct from a **hard fount** and a **soft fount.**

internal memory Memory of a computer which is immediately accessible (i.e., in **RAM** or **ROM** form), as opposed to in external storage (disc, etc.).

internal sizing Alum/rosin, or other synthetic **size** introduced into the papermaking stock at the stock preparation stage to prevent ink spread on printing and writing paper. Also called **engine sizing** or **beater sizing.** As distinct from **external sizing (surface-sizing)** which is carried out at the **size press** on the papermaking machine, and for which different sizing substances are used (often starch).

International Federation of the Periodical Press FIPP International organisation representing magazine printing interests, and author of a useful document on standards in the supply of colour repro material in Europe.

International Organisation for Standardisation (ISO) The organisation which co-ordinates the drawing-up of internationally approved technical standards.

International Standard Book Number See **ISBN**.

internegative Negative for a colour print.

interpositive Photographic positive which will be subject to further camera work to obtain the finished result.

Interpress Rank Xerox's proprietary **page description language**.

interpreter A program **translator** (q.v.). An interpreter resides in memory, takes high-level language program input and translates it to machine-language for the computer every time the program input is run. Compare **compiler** (q.v.) which is a once-and-for-all program to convert high-level language program input into its machine-code equivalent, which then replaces the original in memory.

Intertype Proprietary name of a linecasting machine similar to a **Linotype**.

interword spacing In word processing and desktop publishing, the use of variable interword spacing to achieve justified columns of text. See **intercharacter spacing**.

introduction Introduction to the subject matter of a book (as distinct from **preface, foreword** (q.v.).

Inverform machine Type of paper-making machine used particularly in board making. A series of head boxes feed consecutive layers of wet stock over the main, first, layer at the wet end of the machine to build up a thick final layer of stock on the wire.

inverse video See **reverse video**.

inverted commas See under **quotation marks**.

invert half-tone Gravure printing which uses half-tone dot structures.

I/O Input/Output Relating to systems which can input and output to and from a computer.

iph Impressions per hour. The normal measure of printing speed.

IPSS Abbreviation for International Packet Switching Service: a subscriber international telecommunications **packet-switching** service for the transmission of data on dial-up lines.

IR coating Coating varnish cured by infra-red light.

ISBN International Standard Book Number. A unique 10-digit number that identifies the language of publication of a book, its publisher and its title.

ISDN Integrated Services Digital Network. In communications, an all-digital communications network in which the same lines and switches (exchanges) can be used for different services (voice and data). In the UK, an ISDN service is currently underway, and is scheduled to replace the existing **PSTN** system by the early 1990's.

ISO sizes Formerly **DIN sizes** (q.v.). International range of paper and envelope sizes, comprising **A series**, **B series**, and **C series**.

isolated Advertisement with no other advertisements surrounding it.

ISSN International Standard Serial Number. The periodical equivalent of an **ISBN** (q.v.).

issue All copies of a publication with the same content.

issue life Average reading life of a periodical before it is no longer topical.

italic Specially designed letters that slope forward. Contrast **sloped roman**.

These are italic characters.

Illus 40. Italic letters.

ivory board Fine board manufactured by laminating two high quality sheets together.

J

jacket Dust cover on book.

jacket paper High quality one-sided coated paper used for book jackets.

jacketwrap US term for **jacket paper**.

jaggies See **striations**.

Japanese vellum Paper made in Japan from the bark of the mulberry tree.

jaw folder A type of folder in which a partly folded section is thrust into a jaw to complete its fold. Typically one of the units in a web-offset folder system. Also called a **nip and tuck folder** (q.v.).

JIS Japanese Institute for Standards. The Japanese equivalent to the **ANSI** in the US or the **BSI** in the UK.

jobbing General printing.

job press or **jobbing press** Platen press used for business cards and other small jobs.

jog Align edges of a pile of papers by vibrating them.

joint Recessed part of a book case between the inside edge of the front and back boards and the shoulder, forming a hinge. Also, **French groove**.

jointing The process of forming the **joint** or groove in bookbinding. Also known as **backing** (q.v.).

Jordan Type of paper machine refiner.

joystick A peripheral utilising a multidirectional lever used to move a cursor or to move or alter images on a VDU. Compare **mouse**.

jumbo reel The large reel of paper formed and wound up at the end of a paper-machine.

justification The spacing of words to a predetermined measure, giving 'straight' left and right margins.

justify In word processing and desktop publishing, the use of intercharacter and/or interword spacing to achieve even left and right margins.

jute Indian plant used to produce pulp for especially hard papers.

K

K 1. Abbreviation for 1000. 2. Abbreviation for **kilobyte** (also Kb): a measure of computer storage. Strictly, K = 1024 computer **bytes** but it is often used loosely to indicate 1000.

Kalamazoo Proprietary system of sceduling and listing documents.

kamyr digester Digester used in production of chemical pulp.

K and N absorbency Test for comparing rate of ink absorbency of different papers.

kaolin Fine clay used as a filler in papermaking.

Kb See **kilobyte**.

kb/s In data communications, thousands of bits per second.

keep standing Instruction to the printer to keep all material made up ready for possible reprinting.

kenaf Type of herbaceous plant whose fibres can be used for papermaking (mainly newsprint grades).

kern Part of a typographic character projecting beyond the body.

kerning Adjusting the amount of space to improve the uniformity and appearance of a word or line. See also **character compensation**.

Ti Pa

Illus 41. These characters have been kerned to reduce the space between them and achieve a closer fit.

kerning pairs Pairs of letters which invariably need spacing adjustments made to them for visual neatness. **Autokerning** performs this function automatically (q.v.).

kettle-stitch Stitch joining one signature of a handsewn book to the next. See also **blind stitch**.

key Keyboard text.

keyboard The array of keys used to input into a system.

keyboard dump A printout of all the characters, figures, accents, special sorts, special symbols, codes, etc used in a job, and any relevant descriptions of sequences of keystrokes used to form special characters (eg, for floating accents). A full keyboard dump is an essential aid to a typesetter tackling external files, since he can quickly identify and write search-and-replace programs for any special sorts which need to be typeset.

keyboarding Setting text at a keyboard.

key forme The forme or plate positioned first in colour work. Hence also **key negative**.

keyline Line on artwork which indicates an area for tint-laying, positioning of half-tones etc., or any other area where work must be done at reproduction stage.

key numbers Numbers on advertisements which identify the source in which they appeared.

key plate The printing plate which sets the register position for the other plates.

keystroke One key depression, often used as a measure of productivity of an operator. 10,000 keystrokes per hour (1500 words) is a fairly typical output rate for a trained operator on average work. This equates to around 10,000 words per working day/shift. The keystroke count for a job includes the content of all typesetting and set-up codes as well as the text count itself. Compare **ens of setting**.

keyword The name of a significant category or subject heading under which an article in a book or journal may be classified for database purposes.

kicker Short line above a headline, set in smaller type.

kill Delete unwanted matter. Distribute type.

kilobyte (Kb) One thousand computer **bytes**, or more loosely, characters. As continuous text, in disc storage terms, this works out at around 150 words. Even more approximately, Kb of storage ÷ 3 = A4 pages of average typescript. This table can be taken as a rough guide.

1Kb	150 words	$^1/_3$A4
256Kb	40,000 words	85A4's
512Kb	75,000 words	170A4's
640Kb	95,000 words	210A4's
1Mb	150,000 words	330A4's

kilostream link In the UK, a leased-line (private circuit) capable of supporting data transmission at rates from 2.4K up to 768K baud. See **baud rate**, **megastream link**.

kinetic friction Resistance to sliding of one material over another.

kiss impression Very light printing impression.

kite 'V' shaped plate over which the web of paper is drawn to create first fold.

Kleenstick Proprietary name of pressure-sensitive adhesive-backed paper.

knife folder A type of folding machine which uses a knife between inwardly rotating rollers. Contrast **buckle folder** (q.v.).

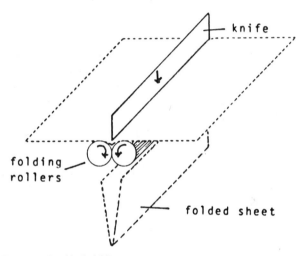

Illus 42. The principle of knife folding.

knocking up To line up the edges of a pile of paper.

kraft Strong brown paper used as a **second lining**, and in many forms of packing application.

kraft pulp See **sulphate pulp**.

Kromecote Proprietary name of a cast-coated paper with glossy finish.

L

label 1. A record which identifies the items stored on a disc or tape. 2. Caption on a technical line drawing.

label paper Paper gummed on one side and usually coated on the other, for labels.

laced-on-boards Signatures of a case-bound book 'laced on' to the case boards.

lacquer Synthetic coating applied to a printed piece for protection or gloss.

laid lines The narrow parallel lines in a laid paper, as opposed to the wider lines at right-angles to these called the **chain lines** q.v.).

laid paper Paper with a pattern of watermarked lines formed by a **dandy roll**. The watermarked lines are of two kinds: **laid lines** and **chain lines**. Laid lines are a pattern of narrow parallel lines formed across the machine direction; chain lines are much wider, broadly spaced lines at right angles to these, and pointing in the machine direction (ie, with the grain). In book printing, the sheet size for laid paper should be specified so that in the finished book the broad chain lines are parallel to the spine of the book (ie, **right-grain**, q.v.).

lamination The application of a thin plastic film by heat and pressure to a printed sheet for protection and/or appearance. See also **OPP lamination**.

lampblack Carbon pigment ink with dull very black appearance.

LAN See **local area network**.

landscape Page format size or illustration that is wider than it is deep. As distinct fom **portrait.**

language In computing, a structured communications vocabulary using codes and words, which can to translated into the machine code which runs the computer. See **high-level language**, **low-level language**.

lap Margin by which one edge of a folded section overlaps the other. A lap is often necessary for the automatic feeding mechanisms into sewing machines.

large post Standard size of paper 419 x 533mm.

laser Acronym for light amplification by stimulated emission of radiation. Concentrated light beam with narrow width used in creating images, engraving, etc.

laser diode The technology used in certain imagesetters which employs a switchable laser beam as opposed to the constant beam of the alternative **helium-neon** laser technology. Helium-neon laser beams are more accurate and are capable of smaller spot sizes; laser diode beams are fractionally less accurate and provide rather larger spot sizes but are cheaper to manufacture.

laser disc See **optical disc**.

laser output unit See **imagesetter**.

laser plotter See **imagesetter**.

laser printer A high-speed non-impact device which employs laser output technology and xerographic techniques to sensitise selected areas of a belt or drum coated with a photosensitive material. As the belt or drum revolves it picks up toner which is transferred to the paper via heated rollers. See also **write white, write black**.

laser recorder See **imagesetter**.

laser setter See **imagesetter**.

laser xerography See **laser printer**.

lasso In DTP, a facility to ring around an illustration or object on the screen and drag it to a new position.

last colour down The final colour to be printed in colour work.

latent image The latent electrostatic image generated by a photocopier and which powder turns into a visible image.

lateral movement In makeready, the movement of a plate from side to side across the plate cylinder as distinct from **circumferential movement** along the circumference of the cylinder.

lateral reversal Change of image from wrong to right-reading or vice versa.

latex Rubber compound added to some paper to improve folding properties.

latex-treated paper Paper impregnated with latex for toughness.

latin alphabet Western European alphabet, as this.

lay Guide on a printing machine which positions a sheet before printing. Hence, **lay edges** (q.v.).

layboy A stacking device on a paper sheeter.

lay down The imposition for a job.

lay edges Edges of a sheet laid against the front and side lays of the machine.

layer-on Machine-minder who feeds sheets to the machine.

layout Sketch of a book or other publication, showing the plan to work to.

lays See **lay**.

l.c. Lower case. See also **U/L, ulc; caps, c&sc.**

L/C See **letter of credit.**

LCD See **liquid crystal display.**

LCL In seafreight, abbreviation for less than a full container load. Consignments sent LCL cost more and take longer than consignments sent **FCL** (q.v.).

leader 1. Row of dots used to lead the eye across a page (also **leader dots, leaders**). 2. See **editorial**. 3. A length of blank paper or magnetic tape used for loading purposes.

lead-in The introduction in a piece of setting, often in a bold or different face.

leading The spacing between lines of type. Also **interlinespacing, film advance, film feed.**

> These are lines of 10pt with no leading.
> These are lines of 10pt with no leading.
>
> These are lines of 10pt with 12pt leading.
> These are lines of 10pt with 12pt leading.
>
> These are lines of 10pt with 14pt leading.
> These are lines of 10pt with 14pt leading.

Illus 43. Variations in leading.

leading edge The edge of a sheet or plate at which printing begins. Also, **gripper edge, pitch edge.**

leaf Single sheet, comprising two pages.

leaflet Folded printed sheet comprising only a few pages.

leather Leathers used in bookbinding include goathides, pigskins, calf-skins, vellum, sheepskins, forels.

leathercloth Bookbinding grade of cloth: a plasticated cotton, dyed-through and calendered.

leather pulp Pulp made from leather scraps and used for **reconstituted leather** coverings.

leave edge The edge of the sheet which leaves the machine last as it goes through the printing rollers into the delivery.

LED See **light-emitting diode**.

ledger paper A strong paper for clerical use.

leg Short column of type.

legend Caption.

legibility The ease with which a page, design or typeface can be read.

length The 'flowability' of a printing ink. **Short** ink does not flow as easily as **long** ink.

Letraset Proprietary name of sheets of transfer lettering.

letter-fit Spacing between characters in a typeface.

Letterflex plate Proprietary letterpress **photopolymer** plate, similar to an **APR** plate.

lettering Hand-drawn typography or a typeface designed to look hand-drawn.

letter of credit L/C A popular export payment instrument which gives a high degree of security to the exporter. On agreement of terms with the exporter, the overseas buyer instructs his local bank to issue a letter addressed to its branch in the exporting country, authorising the latter, providing an agreed set of conditions are fully met, to release payment for goods to the exporter. The set of conditions will lay down the specification for the consignment and the agreed price; it will also carry a time limit for delivery. Procedurally, the terms of a Letter of Credit are best worked out before manufacturing begins. As soon as detailed evidence of the consignment is available − a bill of lading, plus an insurance policy document, plus a commercial invoice for the goods will be the minimum requirement, but sometimes too a certificate of origin, an inspection certificate, and a consular or certified invoice will be needed − payment is made by the exporter's bank immediately. A **Confirmed Irrevocable Letter of Credit** gives maximum security: it carries the payment guarantee of the exporter's bank, and cannot be revoked or altered in any detail unless all four parties to the contract − the buyer, the buyer's bank, the exporter, the exporter's bank − all agree new conditions.

letterpress Printing from images with a raised surface which impresses on the paper.

letter quality Output from printers, typically **daisywheel** printers, that are of a similar quality to office typewriters. Compare **near letter quality**.

letterset Also called **dry offset**, **offset letterpress**, and **indirect letter-press**. A relief plate transfers the image to a blanket and thence on to the paper.

letterspace Space between letters.

letterspacing The introduction of small amounts of space between letters to aid with justification. Typographically undesirable except with capitals, which often benefit from a small amount of letterspacing.

levant Soft, pliable goatskin for bookbinding covers.

Lib Con number See **Library of Congress** number.

library binding Durable type of case binding used on books in libraries.

library buckram The heaviest and best quality form of **buckram** cloth used especially for heavy reference books and library titles.

library material Text or pictures held on file for subsequent use.

Library of Congress number USA system for bibliographical data. The number is printed on the title-page verso.

library sheets Printed sheets in **f&g** form which are sent by the publisher to a specialist library binder.

library supplier Book wholesaler working in the library market, and often commissioning and supplying specially bound library editions instead of standard publisher's editions.

lick-coated paper Paper with a very light coating. Also called **pigmented paper**, **light-coated paper**, **size-press coated paper**.

lift Take typeset material or pictures from elsewhere to reuse.

ligature Two or tied letters joined together on one body, e.g. fi, fl, etc. Contrast **diphthong** (q.v.).

light box Box with glass top illuminated from within so that transparent artwork can be viewed on its surface.

light-coated paper See **size-press coated paper**.

light-emitting diode LED A semiconductor diode which emits light when a voltage is applied. Used in some imagesetters and certain VDU screens.

lightface Lighter version of a roman typeface.

lightfast ink Ink which will fade less readily than normal ink on prolonged exposure to strong light. See **blue wool scale**.

light gate array An array of cells which can be programmed to allow or prevent light passing through to expose photographic material in the creation of an image. Used in some photosetters.

light margin The clear area which must surround a **bar-code** symbol in order for it to be read. Also, **quiet zone**.

light pen Light-sensitive stylus used to edit on a VDU.

light primaries See **additive primaries**.

light secondaries The complementary, or 'opposite' colours to the **additive primaries**.

lightweight coated paper LWC Mechanical coated paper in the range 50gsm-60gsm. See also **ULWC, MWC, HWC**.

lightweight paper Normally taken to mean paper less than 60gsm in substance.

lignin The substance in wood which binds the fibres together. Removed during the pulping process either by mechnical means (incompletely) or chemical means (completely), or a mixture of both. It is the lignin constituent left in mechanical pulp which is responsible for the yellowing with age of mechanical papers.

limp binding Paperback binding.

limp-bound Referring to a book with a limp or paper binding. See also **case-bound**.

line 1. Rule. 2. Copy which consists of solid black lines or dots only, and has no intermediate grey tones. Contrast **tone**.

Lineale Typeface without serifs, otherwise known as **sans-serif**.

line and tone combination An origination made by combining the line elements of an original, shot for line, with the tone elements of the same original which are shot for tone. Hard, sharp outlines are retained as line.

line block A relief plate produced from a line drawing.

line conversion Conversion of continuous-tone copy to line copy by photographing it without a half-tone screen.

line copy Copy which has no gradation of tones, i.e. comprising solid black lines or shapes. Also **line drawing**, **line illustration**, **line engraving**, etc.

line editor A text-processing utility similar to a word-processing program but allowing only line-by-line editing. Often used for editing programs. Contrast a **screen editor** which allows access via the cursor to any part of the screen for corrections to be carried out.

line feed Advancement of paper in a photosetter or printer by one line. Equivalent to **leading**.

line gauge Measuring ruler used for copyfitting and measuring type. Also called **type gauge** and **depth gauge**.

line length Column width of text. Also, **measure**.

line mechanical Paste-up of line copy ready for the camera.

line negative Negative of line illustration or text.

linen finish Imitation linen texture on paper surface.

linen screen Halftone screen giving a linen effect.

line overlay Line work on overlay separate from half-tone.

line printer Output device which prints one line at a time usually with only non-letter-quality resolution.

liner Paper used to cover another paper or board for extra strength, thickness or finish.

linespacing Space between lines of photoset type.

lines per minute A measure of line printer speed.

lines per page Specification of page depth in a book by reference to the number of lines to a page.

lining Part of the spine strengthening in a casebound book. Also, **back lining**. See also **first and second linings**.

lining figs Arabic numerals the same height as capitals, also known as **ranging figs** and **modern figs**. As distinct from **non-lining** or **old-style figs** (q.v.).

THESE ARE LINING FIGURES: 1, 2, 3, 4, 5, 6, 7, 8, 9

Illus 44. Lining figures.

Linofilm Proprietary name of a once-famous but now obsolete photosetter made by Linotype.

Linotron 202 Proprietary name of the most famous of all high-speed third-generation cathode ray tube photosetting machines. Manufactured by Linotype.

Linotronic 300, Linotronic 500 Linotype's two best-selling fourth-generation imagesetters.

Linotype 1. The Linotype corporation, manufacturer of phototypesetting equipment. 2. Name for the hot-metal linecasting machine once manufactured by this company.

lint Surface fibres released from paper during printing.

linting The build-up of lint on an offset blanket causing **hickies** (q.v.) in the printed result. Also, **fluffing** (q.v.), **piling**.

liquid crystal display LCD A display surface consisting of a sandwich of two glass plates and a fluid. The liquid darkens when a voltage is applied, thus creating an image. Used in some imagesetters and (very commonly) in VDU screens.

liquid lamination A high-gloss nitrocellulose varnish applied to book covers or jackets (US).

list All the titles that a publisher has available.

list broker Someone who sells lists of names and addresses in specific market-oriented categories.

listing Computer print-out of data or a file.

listing paper The paper used for computer listings, traditionally printed with light green horizontal stripes and punched with sprocket holes at the sides.

literal Mistake introduced in keyboarding, often only affecting one or two characters.

lith film A high contrast film.

litho See **lithography**.

lithography Litho printing – today's standard printing process. The principle of litho printing is that oil (grease) and water do not mix. The image to be printed is chemically treated to attract greasy litho ink and repel water, whereas the non-image area is chemically treated to do the reverse – attract water and repel ink. To print a litho plate, the plate is first dampened to **desensitise** the non-image area, and then inked: the ink stays only in the image area. In **offset** litho, the image is then printed to a blanket first rather than directly to paper; and then offset from the blanket on to the paper. Shortened to **litho**.

litho prep Litho film assembly and platemaking.

litho varnish See **machine varnish**.

live matter Copy which will go to press rather than be deleted.

loadings Minerals and other fillers added to the furnish of a paper.

loan A rag writing paper.

local area network LAN A network of interfaced peripherals linked by cable over a limited area (e.g. an office), allowing two-way communication between users.

local papers Newspapers circulating in one town or area of the country.

loc cit Abbreviation for Latin 'loco citato' meaning 'in the place cited'. Used as a reference in notes.

lock up 1. To secure metal type in a forme ready for the next stage of production. 2. In program execution, a state from which the system cannot escape.

loft-dried High grade papers dried in a drying shed to allow natural evaporation.

log 1. Log of **small roundwood** (**SRW**), as used in pulp making. 2. Pile of compressed and bundled signatures held in a **ram stacker** or similar.

logo See **logotype**.

Logo An interactive, programming language used mainly in schools to teach computer applications and programming.

log off A computer instruction issued by a user indicating the termination of a session.

log on An instruction, issued by a user, requesting access. A log on sequence will usually include entry of a password.

logoscanner A small **flatbed scanner** which converts a logo, or other special symbol, into digital signals for computer input and displays it on a VDU. The image may then be manipulated or changed in some way before output to a **laser printer**.

Illus 45. A logotype scanned in to the page with a logoscanner.

logotype Company name or product device used in a special design as a trademark. Often shortened to **logo**. See also **colophon**.

long cross The long axis of a sheet of paper. The opposite axis is known as the **short cross**.

long grain Sheet of paper in which the grain direction (or **machine direction**) runs parallel with the longest side.

long grain press A-size web offset press which produces A4 pages in long grain format (with the spine of the publication parallel to the direction of travel of the web and hence parallel to the grain direction of the paper).

long ink An ink that flows easily.

long primer Obsolete type size, approximately 10pt.

long run A high printing number for a job.

long ton Imperial or UK ton (2240lb), equal to 1.12 short (US) tons, or 1.0161 metric tonnes. See **ton**.

look through Appearance of a sheet of paper when held up to the light. Also, **formation** (q.v.). Not to be confused with **show through** (q.v.).

look-up table A table of conditions written as an instruction program. In typesetting, look-up tables are used mainly for hyphenation decisions, fount-width information, and code conversion when text is being transferred from one system to another. Also, **translation table**.

loop Series of computer instructions repeated until a condition is reached which diverts from the loop.

loose leaf Binding which uses steel rings passing through drilled holes in the paper to hold the sheets together.

loose proof Proof of one colour separation out of the four (US).

lower case Small letters as distinct from capitals. Abbreviated as **lc.**

low-level language In computer programming, a language closely related to the **machine-code** of the computer. A low-level language is converted by an **assembler** program into the final machine-code instructions. More efficient than a **high-level language** but more difficult to write.

low resolution Pertaining to a display system using a low number of horizontal and vertical **pixels**. See **pixel, resolution**.

lpi Lines per inch. Common measure of halftone screen rulings (100lpi, 120lpi, 133lpi, etc); but also sometimes used to mean the same as **dpi** (q.v.), or **pixels per inch** in imagesetter output.

LQ Letter quality (applying to a daisy-wheel or laser printer). Compare **NLQ**.

LSI Large scale integration. Referring to **fourth generation computers** which contain high-performance chips, each incorporating from several thousand to a quarter of a million components. See also **VLSI**.

Ludlow Proprietary name of a display-size typecasting machine which uses hand-assembled matrices.

luminous Inks or paints which glow in dark conditions.

Lumitype Proprietary name of a now obsolete filmsetter.

LWC Lightweight coated (paper). Refers to coated papers with a mechanical base in the substance range 50-65gsm. Compare **ULWC, MWC, HWC**.

M

M 1. Abbreviation for 1000, particularly in counting sheets. 2. Abbreviation for **megabyte** (also **Mb**): a computer measure for one million computer bytes. 3. Used to indicate the **machine direction** (grain direction) of a sheet when placed against the appropriate dimension, eg 890 (M) x 1130 is a **short grain** sheet (q.v.).

MacDraw A popular drawing package marketed by Apple for their Macintosh computer.

machine-aided translation The use of a computer to aid translation by relieving the human translator for routine tasks.

machine binding Binding by machine rather than manually.

machine clothing The various felts and wire materials on a paper machine.

machine coated Paper coated on the paper-making machine. Also, **on-machine coated**.

machine code Primary code used by the computer's processor. Few programs are written directly in machine code, but in a **high-level language** or **low-level language** which is then translated by a separate **translator** program into machine code.

machine composition General term for composition of metal type using typecasting equipment.

machine deckle Width of the wet web on a paper-making machine.

machine direction The direction in which fibres lay on the wire of a paper machine, i.e. along the web. Also called **grain direction**. As distinct from the **cross direction** (q.v.).

machine fill A making of paper which uses the full width of the **machine deckle** (q.v.).

machine finished (**MF**) Smooth paper calendered on the paper machine.

machine glazed (**MG**) Glossy finish to one side of paper obtained by drying against the polished surface of a heated cylinder of a Yankee-type paper machine.

machine language See **machine code**.

machine minder Printer who supervises the running of a printing machine.

machine proof Proof made by printing from plates, as opposed to using plastic proofing techniques. Also known as a **wet proof**.

machine readable Data that is in a form that can be read directly by a machine via **floppy disc** or **magnetic tape**.

machine revise Printed sheet for checking against the press proof.

machine varnish Also, **litho varnish**. A low-gloss varnish which can be applied on a printing machine. Used for protection or as a sealant.

machining Printing.

Macintosh See **Apple Macintosh**.

macro A sequence of characters, possibly defined and stored by the user, which may be accessed by the depression of a single key. See also **UDF**.

macron Straight line over a vowel or syllable to indicate that it is long. The opposite of a **breve** (q.v.).

MacWrite A popular word-processing package written by Apple for use on their Macintosh computers.

made ends See **joints**.

mag 1. Magazine. 2. Magnetic (as in tape).

magazine 1. Regularly appearing publication (typically weekly or monthly) covering a subject area with less topicality than a newspaper but with current events and fashions considered. 2. Container for storing matrices of a linecasting machine.

magazine supplement Magazine inserted in a newspaper.

magenta Process red. One of the colours used in four-colour process printing.

magnefite pulp A **sulphite pulp** (q.v.) made using magnesium bisulphite rather than calcium bisulphite in the cooking process. The magnesium waste liquor can be chemically recovered.

magnetic card A word processing recording medium.

magnetic disc A disc with a magnetisable surface coating on to which data may be recorded. See **floppy disc**, **hard disk**, **Winchester disc**.

magnetic head See read-write head.

magnetic ink character recognition The ability of suitable devices to identify characters printed in **magnetic ink**.

magnetic inks Inks with magnetic content that can be read by electronic sensing. Used on cheques.

magnetic tape Narrow tape magnetically coated for the storage in serial form of computer data.

mail box See **electronic mail**.

mailing list List of names and addresses to which mailing pieces can be sent.

mailing piece Promotional material mailed out.

mail merge A word processing utility enabling name and address files to be merged with a text file containing a letter.

mail shot A single sending of promotional material to a list of names and addresses.

mainframe Large computer.

majuscule Capital letter.

makegood Periodical advertisement re-run because the original was faulty.

make-ready Setting up a printing machine ready to run a specific job.

make-up Making-up typeset material into pages.

making In papermaking, a production run of a specific grade of paper on the paper machine. Also, **mill making**.

making order An order for paper to particular specifications needing to be made specially rather than withdrawn from stock.

making-up Assembly of printed sections prior to sewing.

manifold paper A lightweight paper used for copies or for airmail. See also **bank**.

manila A tough paper made from hemp and often used for envelopes.

manual Book giving instructions about a technique or details of operation of a device.

manuscript Abbreviated to **MS**. Typed or handwritten copy for setting. Also **typescript, copy**.

marbled paper Paper covered with a marbled design, used for endpapers of books. True marbled paper is made by hand: paper is dipped into a bath containing liquid pigment colours floating on a viscous gum solution, and then dried. Imitation marbled paper is normal paper printed with this pattern by litho: this is the sort normally used.

marching display Visual display of one line of type displayed sequentially as keyboarded.

margins Areas of white space left around printed matter on a page.

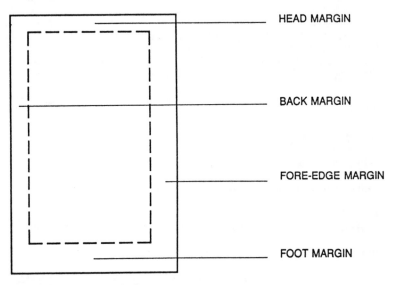

HEAD MARGIN

BACK MARGIN

FORE-EDGE MARGIN

FOOT MARGIN

Illus 46. Page margin terminology.

mark A data circuit impulse corresponding to the active condition of the receiving device. Compare **space**.

marked proof The proof on which the printer's reader has marked corrections.

marking engine The print engine in a laser printer.

markings or **marks** Identifying description written onto a label, e.g. the title of a book on a consignment of paper sent to a printer to show the printer the use for which the paper has been sent.

mark-up Instructions on a layout or copy for the compositor to follow when typesetting or making up pages. See **also electronic mark-up**.

mask Opaque overlay which masks out the unwanted portion of a photograph.

masking In process colour origination using a camera, masking meant the use of colour compensation techniques during the separation process to achieve results more faithful to the original and less liable to colour correction (e.g. applying a **trimask** or other specially made mask to an original to reduce contrast or enhance detail in separate areas and for specific colours). In colour film make-up, masking is the process of marking out specified areas, either electronically or mechanically, which are to undergo tint-laying, reversed out illustration, reversed lettering, etc. See also **unsharp masking**.

masking paper See **goldenrod**.

masking tape A translucent adhesive tape for masking out unwanted areas on film.

massaging Manipulation of copy on a VDU.

massmarket Broadly-based market; in book publishing, general-interest paperbacks.

massmarket paperbacks In publishing, small standard format paperbacks around 178 x 111 in size, normally fiction.

mass storage device Backing storage such as **magnetic disc** or **magnetic drum** which is capable of hoding large amounts of data.

master 1. A plate for a duplication machine: see **paper master**. 2. Original tape, disc, film, etc from which copies will be made.

master proof Printer's proof or reader's proof.See also **marked proof**.

masthead Graphic device which displays a newspaper's name on the front page.

mat See **matrix**.

Matchprint Proprietary dry proof, similar to a **Cromalin**.

matrix Also **matrice**. Mould from which typeface is cast or photographic master of type fount.

matrix printer or **dot matrix printer** One in which each character is represented by a dot pattern. See also **daisywheel printer, laser printer**.

matt or **matte** Dull finish as distinct from glossy.

matt art Coated paper similar to **coated cartridge** in appearance and use but with marginally more calendering and smoothness, and a rather harder surface.

matt coated art See **matt art**.

mature Acclimatise paper to pressroom humidity. Also called **conditioning** (q.v.).

Mb Abbreviation for **megabyte** (q.v.).

McCain sewing See **side-sewing**.

MD In papermaking, **machine direction** (q.v.). As distinct from **CD**, **cross direction**.

mean line Imaginary line which runs along the top of the lower-case letters in a line of text. Also, **x-line**. Compare **base line** (q.v.).

measure Length of line of type. Also, **line length**.

mechanical Camera-ready paste-up (US).

mechanical binding Binding held together by metal or plastic coils. See also **spiral binding**.

mechanical composition See **machine composition**.

mechanical ghosting Ghosting caused by blanket irregularities. Contrast **chemical ghosting**.

mechanical paper Paper made from **mechanical pulp** (q.v.).

mechanical pulp Pulp produced mechanically, by grinding, rather than chemically. There are several sorts. See **stone groundwood mechanical pulp (SGW)**, **refiner mechanical pulp (RMP)**, **thermomechanical pulp (TMP)**, **chemi-thermomechanical pulp (CTMP)**.

mechanical separations Separate colour overlays in register with each other.

mechanical tint Patterned sheet which can produce tonal effects on line work.

media The materials on to which data can be recorded, i.e. **floppy disc**, **magnetic tape**, etc.

media conversion The transfer and conversion of data stored on one type of medium (typically a floppy disc) into the structure and form needed for acceptance by another storage medium (typically a different floppy disc). Carried out by a **media converter** device.

media converter Device which reads from one medium (normally a disc) and translates its content in order to output to another medium (often a disc). See also **multi-disc reader**.

media data form Method of presenting information about a publication for use by advertisers for comparison with other publications.

megabyte Mb One million computer **bytes** or, more loosely, one million characters. As continuous text, in disc storage terms, this works out at around 150,000 words or two average-length novels.

1Mb	150,000 words	330 A4's
6.5Mb	1,000,000 words	2200 A4's
10Mb	1,500,000 words	3300 A4's
20Mb	3,000,000 words	6600 A4's
50Mb	7,500,000 words	16500 A4's
100Mb	15,000,000 words	33000 A4's

See also **kilobyte**.

megahertz One million **hertz**. See **MHz**.

megastream link In the UK, a digital leased-line (private circuit) capable of supporting the transmission of very high volumes of data at high speed, typically 2Mb of data per second or more. Compare **kilostream link**.

melinex Stable polyester base film used for planning.

memory Internal storage of a computer. The memory of a computer is where it finds its instructions and the data it is to work with, as well as where it stores its results. It is organised as a series of locations or cells each of which can hold one computer **word**. The locations are given numbers which enable the computer to identify their positions. See **ROM, RAM**.

menu List of optional procedures displayed at the start of a program.

menu-driven Software program laid out in the initial form of a number of questions to which the operator replies in order to action the program.

merchant In the paper trade, a dealer normally without an affiliation to any particular mill who sells to end-users from a variety of sources.

Merchants can be either **stockist** or **non-stockist** depending on whether they carry their own-risk stock or not.

merge Combine two or more files into one.

metallic inks Inks containing metallic powders to give a gold or silver printed effect. Best printed in conjunction with a **primer** (q.v.).

metamerism In colour printing used to describe the phenomenon whereby certain colours which appear to be all the same hue under one set of lighting conditions then individually change hue under a different set of lighting conditions.

metric system The decimal system of measurement.

mezzotint Form of print created by removing a roughened surface to a greater or lesser degree from a specially burred metal plate, thus creating areas of continuous tone; used to simulate the effect of painting. By extension, a form of half-tone **screen** (q.v.) which imitates this effect.

MF See **machine finished**.

MG See **machine glazed**.

MHz One million **hertz** (q.v.). Most micros are ruled between 5-20 MHz in microprocessor speed.

MICR Magnetic ink character recognition.

MICR paper Magnetic ink character recognition paper.

microchip See **chip**.

microcomputer Small computer, usually without multi-user capabilities except when forming part of a **network** (q.v.). Its central processing unit is typically a single-chip **microprocessor** (q.v.).

microdisc Small rigid microcomputer disc, normally 3.5" in diameter. Also called, rather misleadingly, **microfloppy disc**.

microelite Small size of typewriter type: 15 characters per inch.

microfiche Sheet film, typically 105x150mm, containing on it a large number of pages of information photographically reduced to very small size and readable only with a **microfiche reader**.

microfilm Photographic film with a greatly reduced image. Microfilms are used in **projection platemaking equipment** systems (q.v.).

	UK unit	Multiplication factor	Metric
Length	inches	2.54000	centimetres
	feet	0.3048	metres
	yards	0.9144	metres
	miles	1.609344	kilometres
Weight	ounces	28.3495	grams
	pounds	0.45359	kilograms
	short tons (2 000 lbs)	0.907185	tonnes
	long tons (2 240 lbs)	1.01605	tonnes
Area	sq inches	6.4516	sq centimetres
	sq feet	0.092903	sq metres
	sq yards	0.836127	sq metres
	sq miles	2.58999	sq kilometres
	acres	0.404686	hectares
Capacity and volume	cu inches	16.387064	cu centimetres
	pints	0.5683	litres
	gallons	4.546	litres
Velocity	miles per hour	1.609344	kilometres per hour
	feet per second	0.3048	metres per second
Temperature	degrees Fahrenheit	$(-32) \times \frac{5}{9}$	degrees Celsius

Illus 47. Metric conversion tables.

microfloppy disc A floppy disc which is less than 5.25 inches in diameter. The size in commonest use is 3.5 inch. Such discs are in fact not floppy at all as they are encased in rigid plastic envelopes.

microform Generic term for **microfiche** and **microfilm**.

micrometre One-thousandth of a millimetre. Also, **micron**.

micron Alternative term for **micrometre**.

microprocessor The central processing unit (**CPU**) of a microcomputer: an integrated circuit typically housed on a single chip which contains the control unit, the arithmetic and logic unit, and some memory. See also **chip, CPU, microcomputer**.

microsecond One-millionth part of a second. Measurement used in computing. Compare **millisecond, nanosecond, picosecond**.

Microsoft American software house, most famous as writers (in collaboration with IBM) of **MS-DOS** for IBM-compatible micros; for **MS Word**, a popular word-processing package; and for numerous other programs.

microspheres Small chemical spheres which can be added to a papermaking furnish, and which swell during the making process to give extra volume to the paper.

middle space or **mid space** A space equal to one-quarter of a **mutton** or em space.

mid tones or **middle tones** Tonal ranges between highlights and shadows.

mill agent In the paper trade, a mill's representative, often in an importing country, through whom the mill's sales are made. Mill agents may have exclusive or non-exclusive representation rights to their mill's products.

millboard True millboard is a very dense, hard board used in stationery binding and for archival use. The term millboard is sometimes used to describe normal caseboards, which are more properly **grey board** or **unlined chipboard** (q.v.).

mill conditioned Paper conditioned for normal atmospheric humidity. See **conditioning**.

mill finished See **machine finished**.

mill glazed See **machine glazed**.

millisecond One-thousandth part of a second. Measurement used in computing. Abbreviated to **ms**. Compare **microsecond, nanosecond, picosecond**.

mill making See **making**.

mini See minicomputer.

mini-cassette Used as a backing storage device, usually in smaller portable computers. These cassettes are similar in design to those used in pocket dictation machines.

minicomputer Small but powerful computer, usually dedicated to one job rather than general data processing.

minifloppy disc A name given to 5.25 inch floppy discs. to identify them as different from 8 inch floppy discs. As 5.25 inch discs became the type in widest use the term fell into misuse.

minion Obsolete term for 7pt type.

mini-web Small web offset machine typically producing 16pp A4 colour sections (8p A4 to view). Also known as **narrow-web**, or **half-size** press.

minuscule Lower-case letter.

mips Millions of instructions per second. Measurement of computer processing speed.

misprint Typographical error.

misregister One colour or more printed out of alignment with other colours.

mitre 45 degree angle join at corners of metal rules.

mixed furnish Referring to papers which have mechanical and woodfree pulps in their furnish. See **part-mechanical**.

mixing Usually applied to typefaces of different founts in one line of text.

mnemonic codes Easily remembered codes: abbreviations or tags which suggest their meanings (bd1 = bold style 1, for example).

mock-up A layout or rough of artwork. Also called a **visual**.

modem or **Modulator/Demodulator** Device which converts analogue communication (eg, telephone transmission) into digital form and vice versa. Modems are necessary on conventional **PSTN** telephone networks because the lines only support analogue transmission, not digital transmission. The newer digital telephone networks (**ISDN** lines) which are steadily replacing the analogue PSTN lines support digital transmission and do not need modems.

Modern Category of nineteenth century typestyle also called **Didone** and exemplified by such faces as Bodoni and Modern Extended.

abcdefghijklmnopqrstuvwxyz
ABCDEFGHIJKLMNOPQRSTUVWXYZ
1234567890 1234567890 .,;:'"«»&!?

Illus 48. Bodoni, an example of a Modern type style.

modern figs See **lining figs**.

modular Hardware system capable of being exanded by adding on compatible devices.

modular press See **unit press**.

moiré Undesirable pattern caused by incorrect angles of screens.

moisture content Amount of moisture in paper, expressed as a percentage of weight. A moisture content of around 7-8% is recommended for printing papers in optimum press room conditions (20⁰C, 55-65% RH).

moisture welts Wrinkles in a paper roll caused by moisture absorption after drying.

molleton Cotton material used on damping rollers.

monitor Screen which displays the operations of a machine in real time.

mono See **black and white**.

monochrome One colour (usually meaning black and white).

monoline Typeface with all strokes appearing to have the same thickness, e.g. Univers.

monograph Scholarly work on a particular subject.

Monophoto Proprietary name of a famous second-generation phototypesetter manufactured by the Monotype corporation.

monospaced Letters which have all the same set widths, as in typewriter faces or **non-wysiwyg** VDU screen displays.

monotone Illustrative material in one colour.

Monotype 1. The Monotype corporation, British manufacturers of type-setting equipment. 2. Proprietary name for Monotype's hot-metal type-casting machine which assembles characters individually rather than line-by-line.

montage Several images assembled into one piece of artwork.

morgue Newspaper reference library.

morocco Goatskin with fine grain for bookbinding.

motherboard The printed circuit board containing the main components of a computer. See **add-on board, expansion board**.

mottle Uneven printing in solid areas caused by poor ink or uneven absorption characteristics in the paper.

mould See **matrix**.

mould-made paper Paper either made by hand, or made on a **cylinder mould machine** (q.v.).

mount Base of wood or metal which supports a letterpress printing plate.

mouse Small electronic puck which may be moved laterally and vertically on a plain flat surface to control the movement of a cursor on a VDU screen. See also **puck, tracker ball**.

mouse mat Specially smooth and dirt-resistant mat on top of which a **mouse** can be manipulated.

ms See **millisecond**.

MS See **manuscript**.

MS-DOS Microsoft's Disc Operating System. The **operating system** of IBM PC clones. See also **DOS** and **PC-DOS**.

MS Word A popular word-processing package, closely associated with the AppleMac environment. Its main rivals include Apple's own word-processor, MacWrite, and WordPerfect. The other main word-processing competitor (but more in the IBM PC environment) is WordStar.

mull Muslin fabric fixed to the back of a case bound book under the spine covering. See **first and second linings**. See illustration overleaf.

multicode One keystroke which generates several commands.

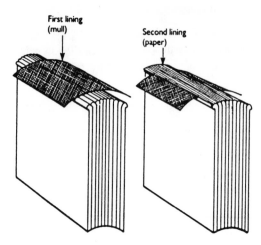

First lining
(mull)

Second lining
(paper)

Illus 49. Mull, a lining on the spine of a case bound book.

multicolour keyline artwork Baseboard artwork with overlays to show the divisions of the colours.

multicolumn setting Typesetting to a page design which features several columns across (as in a newspaper).

multi-disc reader Machine which reads a variety of discs in different formats and translates their content to output discs. Also, **media converter**.

multi-layer headbox In papermaking, a **headbox** (q.v.) which distributes up to three different layers of stock on to the wire simultaneously.

Multilith Proprietary name of a small offset press in wide use.

multimetal plates Litho printing plates made from two or three layers of metal for extra durability. See **bimetal plates, trimetal plates**.

multiplexor In data communications, a switching device which allows one common transmission facility, for example a leased-line, to be used as a number of separate **channels** appearing to operate independently and simultaneously. In reality, the multiplexor at the sending end of a common circuit switches and controls the signals coming from a number of channels, combining them into one common channel; and the multiplexor at the receiving end extracts and divides each of the original signals to send them to their proper destinations. Sometimes called **asynchronous multiplexor**.

multiprocessing Computer operation of several tasks simultaneously.

multistage bleaching The bleaching of pulp by passing it through successive tanks of bleach chemicals.

multi-tasking Performing several tasks simultaneously, using a single microcomputer.

multi-user Computer system allowing multiple users access to the same machine, software and data files.

mump To move/copy founts between one typesetting house and another.

Munsell system A colour gradation system which uses numbers for identification.

mutton An em quad.

MWC Medium weight coated. A category of mechanical coated paper in the substance range 65-85gsm. See also **ULWC, LWC, HWC**.

mylar Stable polyester film base often used for planning positive films.

N

nanometre One-thousand-millionth part of a metre. Abbreviated to **nm**.

nanosecond One-thousand-millionth part of a second. Measurement of computer processing speed. Abbreviated to ns. Compare **millisecond, microsecond, picosecond**.

nap roller Leather-covered ink roller.

narrowband transmission In data communications, transmission along a channel with a low band width only capable of supporting data transmission at speeds less than 300 baud. Contrast **broadband transmission**.

narrow web See **mini-web**.

national press Newspapers with a countrywide circulation.

natural Description of a kind of case-covering material finish.

NCR Proprietary name of a paper which, being impregnated with dye, transfers an image on to the sheet below when written on or typed on.

NC varnish Nitrocellulose varnish: a high-gloss varnish applied to book covers.

near letter quality (NLQ). The top level of quality that can be obtained by **dot matrix printers**. An attempt is made to emulate the output of **daisywheel** printers usually by printing a line in the usual way and then reprinting the line to enhance the characters by the addition of serifs, for example.

```
This is an example
of near letter quality
produced from an
Epson dot matrix
printer.
```

Illus 50. Near letter quality emulates daisywheel output.

nearside lay The sidelay on the operating side of the press, ie the left-hand side of the press as viewed from the feed end. See also **offside lay, lay**.

neckline White space under a headline.

needle printer Another term for **matrix printer**.

neg-and-print Describes a photographic print made from an original by shooting a negative and then making a contact print from this, rather than shooting the original to **PMT**. Better quality can be expected from a neg-and-print print, since there is an opportunity for retouching at the negative stage.

negative Reverse photographic image on film.

negative assembly Combining negatives on a **flat** ready for platemaking.

negative-positive print The standard colour 'en' print.

negative-working plates Litho plates which are exposed using negatives.

nest To place a program routine within a larger routine, or to place a file or group of files within a directory.

net With no discount allowed.

net book agreement Agreement in the publishing and bookselling trades to sell books at the retail price dictated by the publisher. An example of retail price maintenance.

net profit In book publishing terms, the final profit achieved after the overhead costs involved in producing the title are deducted from its **gross profit**, ie, total sales revenues less production costs, royalties, direct promotion costs, salaries, occupancy, distribution overheads, etc.

network An arrangement of linked computers which typically draw on a common database of information resident on a **fileserver** while retaining considerable local processing capabilities.

neuron chip Highly advanced programmable microchip with functions approaching artificial intelligence.

neutral sized paper Paper which is internally or externally sized with neutral pH7, acid-free, size so that at the time of delivery it is free of acid content. Neutral sizing gives a paper considerable qualities of longevity, but its use does not in itself fulfil the full requirement for it to be termed **permanent paper** as in the US standard for this (q.v.).

news chase Special chase of newspaper-page size which incorporates its own locking mechanism.

newspaper Publication containing topical reportage.

newspaper lines per minute nlpm Standard measure of photosetter speeds. Specifically, output measured in 8pt lines to an 11em measure.

newsprint Paper made from mechanical pulp for the printing of newspapers, usually between 45 and 58gsm.

news stall circulation Periodical distribution through retail newsagents as distinct from the mail.

next to editorial Instruction to position advertisement adjacent to editorial text.

nick Groove in metal type which appears uppermost during assembly.

nickletype An electrotype plated with nickel.

nip Pressure point between two rollers.

nip and tuck folder See **jaw folder, folder.**

nipping Pressing a book to flatten the signatures and remove air from between the sheets. This takes place after the bookblocks are sewn and before they are rounded and backed, and sent on for further processing. Also known as **crushing** or **smashing.**

NLQ Near letter quality, as applied to a dot-matrix printer. Used to describe fair quality output from higher-resolution dot-matrix printers. Betwen **draft quality** and **letter quality** output in standard (q.v.).

nm A **nanometre** (q.v.).

no break area In text setting, a defined sequence of words or characters within which hyphenation is disallowed for grammatical or contextual reasons.

no flash Photosetting command which prevents exposure of characters. Used to create space of specific length.

noise Disturbance on an electrical circuit.

nominal weight American system of specifying **basis weight** (q.v.) of paper.

non-consumable textbook Textbook which will be re-used constantly rather than written in.

non-counting keyboards Keyboards which cannot access justification logic and whose output therefore must be further processed by a CPU.

non-destructive cursor A VDU cursor that can be moved about the screen without altering or destroying displayed characters.

non-impact printing Electronic methods of image transfer without striking paper. See **ink jet printer, laser printer**.

non-lining figs See **old-style figs**.

nonpareil Obsolete term for 6pt type.

non-ranging figs See **old-style figs**.

non-reflective ink Light-absorbing ink used to print machine-readable characters.

non-reproducing blue See **drop-out blue**.

non-scratch inks Inks resistant to marking.

non-standard formats In book production, those book formats which fall outside the conventional range of formats obtainable from the standard metric range of papers.

non-tarnish paper Paper free from chemicals which will tarnish metal surfaces in contact with it.

non-volatile memory Memory (e.g. **bubble memory**) that retains information when the power supply is removed.

non-woven material See **imitation cloth**.

non-wysiwyg The standard typewriter-style display of words on a computer screen, as opposed to the **wysiwyg** 'printed' style associated with DTP.

Nordsen binder Device which applies a line of glue beneath the shoulder of a bookblock to reinforce the casing-in process. Useful for heavy books.

no-sheet detector A sensing mechanism which automatically trips the press out of impression if a sheet either arrives late or fails to arrive.

notch binding A form of unsewn binding in which notches are punched in the backs of the sections as they are folded on the folding machine, and glue applied in through the notches to hold the leaves together. Also called **slotted binding**. See also **burst binding**.

np In proof-reading, new paragraph: an instruction to start a new para.

ns A nanosecond (q.v.).

null In computing, an all-zero setting, eg 00000000. Often used as a switch to indicate that a code is the next signal following.

numbering machine On or off-press device which numbers printed sheets consecutively, e.g. for tickets.

nut An en quad.

nutmegging In web offset printing, the formation of unwanted fine and smudged dot patterns in small areas caused by ink transfer from a **grater roller** carrying the web of paper (q.v.).

O

OBA Optical bleaching agent: a chemical which is used in the furnish of bright-white papers to enhance their brightness, and which does so by converting ultraviolet light into visible light.

OBC Outside back cover.

object code or **object language** Machine code, as translated from a **source program** (q.v.).

object program Program in machine code translated from a **source program** (q.v.).

oblique 1. Slanted roman characters. 2. The forward slash symbol '/', also called a **solidus** or **slash**. As distinct from the **backslash** symbol '\'.

oblong Format in which the binding edge is shorter than the width of a book, as contrasted with the more conventional **portrait** format for a book. Also called **landscape**.

OCR Optical Character Recognition. The interpretation of typewritten or printed characters by a machine which scans the text and stores it in memory, often for subsequent typesetting. See also **ICR**.

OCR-A A typeface designed to aid machine readability. Compare **OCR-B**.

OCR-B A machine-readable typeface that is designed to be more legible to humans than **OCR-A**.

OCR paper High-quality bond suitable for optical character recognition equipment.

octal Mathematical system with a base of 8. Compare **hexadecimal, binary**. Our normal numbering system is **decimal**.

octavo Abbreviated as 8vo. The eighth part of the traditional **broadside** sheet. Used to describe book sizes, e.g. Demy Octavo.

oddment A book signature with fewer pages than the others and which has to be printed separately.

OEM Original Equipment Manufacturer. An **OEM product** is one which is a rebadged and possibly enhanced version of an original manufactured product, and which sells under its rebadged name.

OFC Outside front cover.

offcut A remnant of a sheet of paper cut off from its original dimension.

off-line Mode of computer peripheral operation in which equipment is not physically linked to a CPU and must be operated through an intermediate medium.

off-line typesetting systems Typesetting system configurations in which the text entry is performed at separate free-standing machines (typically micros) and the files are relayed to the main system via floppy disc at a later stage. Contrast **on-line typesetting systems**.

off-machine coating Coating applied to a paper as a separate operation. Contrast **on-machine coating**.

offprint Part of a book or journal printed separately, e.g. an article from a journal.

offset Printing which uses an intermediate medium to transfer the image on to paper, e.g. a rubber blanket wrapped around a cylinder as in offset litho.

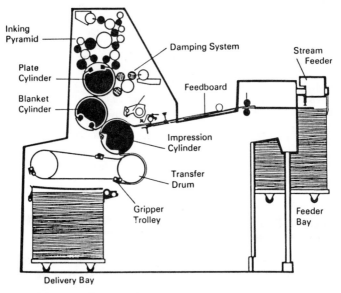

Illus 51. An offset litho press.

offset cartridge Standard uncoated printing paper from around 85gsm upwards suitable for litho printing.

offset letterpress See **letterset**.

offset lithography See **offset**.

offset paper Any paper suitable for offset litho printing.

offside lay The lay opposite the operating side of a press. As distinct from **nearside lay** (q.v.).

OKWC OK with corrections. Instruction to a typesetter to make corrections and then proceed to next stage.

Old Face Classic typestyle designs of the 16th and 17th centuries. Also called **Garalde** (q.v.).

Old Style Nineteenth and twentieth century revival forms of **Old Face** typestyles exemplified by Old Style and Imprint.

abcdefghijklmnopqrstuvwxyz
ABCDEFGHIJKLMNOPQRSTUVWXYZ
1234567890 .,;:'"«»&!?

Illus 52. Old Style.

old-style figs Also called **non-lining figs** or **non-ranging figs**. Numerals which do not align on the base line but have ascenders and descenders. As distinct from **modern** or **lining figures**.

omni-directional scanning Scanning at any orientation.

on-demand publishing The concept of printing books one at a time from computer store 'on demand', rather than tying up capital by printing for stock.

one-letter index Index with divisions by letter (but often including x, y, and z together).

one-piece films Final contact films for platemaking, as distinct from **composite films** which may be made up of several film pieces taped or cemented together.

one-shot binding Perfect binding with one applicaton of hot-melt glue only. As distinct from **two-shot binding** (q.v.).

one-sided art Paper coated on one side only (such as jacket art).

one-way screen Half-tone screen with the lines one-way only vertically.

onionskin Lightweight cockle finish blank paper often used for airmail stationery.

on-line Connected direct to a central processing unit and communicating with it.

on-line typesetting systems Typesetting systems in which the keyboards are attached at all times on-line to the main system computer and can access files from it. Common in newspaper systems.

on-machine coating Coating applied to the base paper on the paper-machine itself. As distinct from **off-machine coating**, where the base paper is coated as a completely separate operation, giving a superior result.

on the fly Refers to any process which occurs as output is being performed, such as the screening of half-tones simultaneously with output to an image recorder.

opacity The quality of opaqueness in a paper. Opacity is measured in %, with around 88-90% being an average for 80g/m2 printing paper. Rather confusingly two pieces of testing equipment (and so two sets of scale units) are in use: the EEL Opacimeter and the Zeiss Elrepho. Readings in EELs tend to be slightly lower than readings in Elrepho.

opaque 1. To paint out areas on film with an opaque paint. 2. The paint used in opaquing, also called **photopaque**.

opaque printing An MF printing paper with high opacity

op cit Abbreviated Latin 'opera citato' meaning 'in the work cited'. Used with an author's name to indicate a work already referred to.

open architecture In computer system design, the ability to allow for extra peripherals in order to expand the system at any time in the future.

opening A pair of facing pages.

opening and closing quotes In typography, opening and closing quotation marks in speech, set either as single inverted commas before or after the affected passage arranged in '6 and 9' format, or as double inverted commas arranged in "66 and 99" format.

open time In binding, the time between an adhesive being applied and when it sets. In printing, the time an ink stays fluid on the press.

operand In computing, an item of data on which an operation is to be carried out.

operating system A basic set of software utilities usually supplied as

firmware that control the operation of user programs.

operation Result of a computer command.

OPP lamination Oriented polypropylene **lamination** (q.v.). The standard book-jacket lamination film.

optical brightener or **optical brightness agent** Dye which emits visible radiation. Used to 'brighten' paper.

optical centre The 'visual' centre of a page, about 10% higher than the mathematical centre.

optical character recognition See **OCR**.

optical density Light-absorbing capacity of an image area.

optical disc Generic term for a high-density storage device, mainly of the read-only variety. The characterising feature is that the information is read off the disc using laser (optical) technology, rather than the electromagnetic technology of tapes and discs. The two main subgroups are **video discs** (q.v.) on which the information is stored in an analogue manner for visual moving display (television); and **optical digital discs** on which information is stored digitally. **CD** discs are in this second subgroup (q.v.).

optical letterspacing Space between letters which accommodates their varying shapes and gives the appearance of even space.

orange peel Multi-indentation effect on paper.

order form Form on which a buyer can fill in the detail of his intended purchase as an order to supply.

orientation Positioning in relation to normal horizontal and vertical alignment.

oriented polypropylene OPP A form of extruded polypropylene film commonly used for lamination. Waterpoof and flexible.

original Photograph or drawing to be reproduced.

original plate Letterpress plate produced by photo-mechanical etching as distinct from sterotyping.

origination All the processes involved in the reproduction of original material, including make-up, up to plate-making stages; and also including typesetting. See also **repro**.

ornamented Typeface embellished with decorative flourishes.

Illus 53. An ornamented A.

orphan The first line of a new paragraph, or a subhead, which appears at the foot of a page. Considered undesirable. Contrast **widow, clubline.**

orthochromatic film Photographic material insensitive to red and sensitive to blue (ie, seeing blue as white). The standard type of phototypesetting film and origination film. Film which is sensitive to all colours is called **panchromatic film.**

OS/2 Operating System/2. Microsoft's operating system for the IBM PS/2 (Personal System/2) family of computers.

outer forme The imposed forme which forms the outside of the sheet when folded and which therefore contains the first page of the section. Contrast **inner forme.**

outline Typeface comprising only an outline with no 'solid' area. Contrast also **inline**, in which the characters have white inner areas against a bolder outline shape.

This is an outline typeface

Illus 54. An outline typeface.

out of focus Blurred, not properly focussed by a camera.

out of register One or more colours out of alignment with the others in a piece of printing.

out of round Distorted paper reel.

output Data or any form of communication coming out of a computer after processing.

output scanner The output half of a colour scanner which records the image on to film, typically by laser. Also known as **output recorder**, or **exposure unit**, or **plotter.**

outsert Item of promotional material on the outside of, rather than inside, a pack or periodical.

out-turn sheet Sheet of paper taken during manufacture or on delivery as a representative sample for checking specification.

outwork Operations put out to another company for reasons of specialism or capacity.

overdraw In colour masking and assembly, the fractional enlarging of an image which is reversed out of another, so that its outer borders fit under the surrounding image to prevent the risk of white fringes. See also **choke.**

overexposure Too lengthy an exposure of film, causing a thin, 'chipped', image. **Underexposure** (q.v.) leads to a dense, dark, murky image.

overhang cover Cover larger than the text pages. Also **overlap cover** or **yapp cover.**

overlay 1. Transparent cover to artwork containing instructions or additional detail. 2. Paper used on machine cylinder to increase pressure on solid areas of blocks.

overmatter Typeset matter which is too long to fit the space specified and so must be cut. Also called **overset.**

overprinting An additional printing over a previously printed sheet. See **colour blanks.**

overrun Copies printed in excess of the specified printing number.

overs See **spoilage.**

overset Alternative term for **overmatter.**

oversewing Attaching single leaves to a sewn book with thread sewing.

overstocks Surplus stocks.

overstrike A method by which a word processor might produce a character not in its character set. For example, a Yen symbol could be produced by printing a 'Y' and overstriking an 'equals' symbol.

Oxford hollow A **hollow** (q.v.) on the back of a book which consists of a tube of brown paper attached to the back of the folded sections and the inside of the case hollow. Used for heavy books where reinforcement is necessary.

oxidation Chemical action with the oxygen in the air: one of the principal ways in which sheet-fed offset ink dries. Oxidation also affects litho plates, attacking the non-image area and leaving minute spots of surface corrosion. **Gumming up** a plate helps prevent this.

ozalid Print made by a form of diazo copying process and often used for proofing film. See also **blueprint**.

P

package Set of software bought 'off-the-shelf' rather than specifically commissioned.

package insert Promotional material contained with a product's packaging.

packager Company which provides complete publications ready to be marketed.

packet switching network Computer-controlled data communications network in which data is divided into digital 'packets' transmitted at high speed.

packing Paper or plastic sheets placed next to the impression cylinder in letterpress, or under the plate or blanket in litho, to adjust printing pressure.

packing density Amount of information which can be stored on a magnetic medium.

page One side of a leaf.

page count Synonym for **extent** (US).

page description language PDL In desktop publishing, a computer language allowing the description and formation of combined text and graphics, encompassing factors such as scaling, fount rotation, graphics and angles. Some examples, such as Adobe's **PostScript**, are device-independent. Other PDLs include **Interpress** from Xerox, **DDL** from Imagen Corporation and Interleaf's RIP print.

PageMaker Pre-eminent page make-up program designed by **Aldus** (q.v.) for running on the Apple Macintosh computer.

page make-up Assembly of the elements of a page into their final design. Page make-up may be carried out either manually using repro galleys or PMTs (**cut and paste**); or in the case of material held as a computer file, by batch instruction via a page make-up program (**batch pagination**); or interactively at the computer VDU (**interactive page make-up** or **screen make-up**).

page make-up terminal A specialised desktop publishing workstation used to assemble type and graphics in finished page form for output as a piece.

page printer One which composes a complete output page before printing it. Compare **line printer**.

page proof Proof of a page before printing.

page pull test Test to determine the strength of binding of an adhesive bound book.

page scrolling The movement, on a VDU, of an entire page (or screen) of data.

pages per inch Number of pages per inch of thickness. US measurement of bulk. Abbreviated **ppi**.

pages to view The number of pages on a printing plate, and therefore on one side of a printed sheet.

page traffic Readership of a given page of a publication calculated as a percentage of total readership.

page view terminal VDU which can display a page in its made-up form.

pagination Page numbering.

paging Scanning text on a VDU page by page.

Pagitek A popular professional page make-up system marketed by Miles.

palbox or **pallet box** Strong export carton whose base is built like a pallet for easy loading.

palette A computer graphics feature which allows the user to select colours from a displayed selection, possibly including the ability to mix two or more colours.

pallet Wooden base on which paper or books are stored. Also known as **skid** and **stillage**. The 'European standard' pallet size is 1000x1200mm, four-way entry. A maximum pallet weight of 1000kg and maximum height of 1219mm (4 feet) are commonly specified. Typical pallet loads might come to 1000-1250 books of average octavo size; or around 12500 sheets of quad demy (one tonne in 80gsm).

pamphlet Booklet comprising only a few pages.

pamphlet binding See **saddle stitching**.

panchromatic film Photographic material sensitive to all colours.

panel Display board.

pantograph Mechanical apparatus for copying a line drawing.

Pantone Proprietary name of a widely used colour-matching system.

paper basis weight See **basis weight**.

paperboard Lightweight board in the range 200gsm-300gsm. See **board**.

paper master Paper plate used on small offset machine.

paper surface efficiency (**PSE**) Printability of a paper.

paper tape Strip of paper which records data as a series of punched holes arranged in 'channels' or 'tracks' across the width.

papeterie Smooth, stiff paper used in greeting card manufacture.

papier mache Repulped paper with stiffening additives which can be used for moulding.

papyrus Egyptian reed from which the earliest form of paper was made.

paragraph indent In typesetting a paragraph indent is conventionally one **em** of set.

paragraph opener Typographic device marking the start of a paragraph which needs emphasising.

> ● This paragraph has a paragraph opener. This particular one (a 'bullet' or 'cannonball') is widely used to indicate items in a list.

Illus 55. A paragraph opener.

paragraph widow A very short line (one or two words) appearing as the last line of a paragraph anywhere on a page. To be avoided if possible. Usually more unacceptable is the **page widow** (q.v.).

parallel folding Folding a sheet with all the folds parallel to each other. Contrast **right-angle folding**.

parallel interface In computing, any form of information exchange that transmits characters along several data lines (typically seven or eight), one bit per line, in parallel. See **parallel transmission**.

parallel transmission Data communications method where each **bit** in the computer byte travels in parallel with its fellows along its own line so that bytes arrive intact. (Contrast **serial transmission** in which a single line is used for transmission and the bits are transmitted sequentially). Parallel transmission is faster than serial transmission and is widely used for transmission to printers. See also **Centronics interface**.

parameter In computing, a variable which can be set to a particular value for the duration of a specific operation.

parentheses Round brackets.

parity bit An error-detection or check bit added to a series of binary digits to make the total odd or even according to the logic of the system. It is used for checking and verification purposes.

part-mechanical paper Paper containing up to 50% of mechanical pulp with the balance chemical pulp. Compare **mechanical paper, woodfree paper**.

partwork Publication issued in a number of parts which can be purchased separately and which then combine to make up the whole.

pass 1. One run through a machine. Also, **working**. 2. An operation that realises the completion of a job from input through processing to output.

pass date See **copy date**.

pass for press Authorise the final form of a publication for printing.

passim Throughout (in references).

pass-on rate Estimated number of readers of a publication per copy sold.

password A character string, unique to the user and usually not displayed on any system peripheral, used to gain access to a system or a protected file or files within a system.

pasteboard or **pasted board** Board made from several laminations of thinner sheets. Contrast **homogenous board** (q.v.).

paste drier Type of drier used in inks. It contains metallic salts and is formulated to dry an ink without hindering the trapping properties of the next ink film on top of it.

pasted unlined chipboard See **unlined chipboard**.

pastel boost Facility on a colour scanner to enhance pastel shades.

paster See **flying paster**.

paste-up Rough dummy or camera-ready artwork comprising all the elements of a job pasted into position either forr visual purposes, as a layout guide, or as camera-ready copy for shooting.

patch 1. Sub routine inserted into a program after writing. 2. A few lines of typesetting intended for pasting in to an artwork or CRC.

patch corrections Small patches of corrected typesetting which are intended for pasting over the original (wrong) text.

patching Pasting corrections into film or artwork.

patching-up Letterpress packing during make-ready.

patent base Base on which **electrotypes** (q.v.) are mounted.

pattern matching systems Intelligent **OCR** systems capable of scanning and recognising letters in running text by determining the patterns of letterform design, rather than working from stored and fixed-format fount templates held in memory as in the less sophisticated **template-matching** systems.

PBA Periodicals Barcoding Association.

PC personal computer Microcomputer for home or office use.

pcb Abbreviation for **printed circuit board**.

pcc Abbreviation for precipitated calcium carbonate: see under **calcium carbonate**.

PC-DOS Version of Microsoft's Disc Operating system specific to the IBM PC. Slight, mainly insignificant, variations from **MS-DOS** (q.v.).

PCL Abbreviation for **Printer Control Language**, the Hewlett Packard laser printer control code set.

PDL See **page description language**.

PE printer's error Error introduced during the keyboarding or formatting of a text, and liable for correction by the typesetter at his own expense.

pebble finish Textured surface on paper, added after making or sometimes after printing.

pebbling Embossing paper after printing with a pebbled pattern.

peculiars Special characters outisde a normal fount range.

pel See **pixel**.

penetration One of the ways in which inks dry. See **absorption**.

pen ruling Method of printing ruled sheets with a set of pens, under which the sheet travels.

percentage dot area The percentage of a half-tone that is black as opposed to white.

perfect binding Adhesive binding widely used on paperbacks. Glue is applied to the roughened back edges of sections to hold them to the cover and each other. Also called **adhesive binding, cut-back binding, thermoplastic binding, threadless binding**.

perfecting Printing both sides of a sheet at one pass. Such a press is called a **perfector**. The opposite - printing one side of a sheet at a time - is known as **straight printing**.

perforated tape See **paper tape**.

perforating Punching a series of holes in paper, either as a coding process or to facilitate tearing off a part.

perforating rules Letterpress steel rules which indent the sheet.

perforator Keyboard which produces punched paper tape.

period (US) Full stop.

peripheral Computer input or output device which is not part of the main pc unit, eg, a printer.

permanence Paper's resistance to ageing.

permanent inks Inks which do not fade. Also, **lightfast inks** (q.v.).

permanent paper Paper which is **acid-free** and made to stringent conditions for archival purposes. The accepted standard for manufacture is laid out in American standard ANSI Z39 1984 and specifies neutral pH, alkaline reserve (extra buffer), an entirely chemical pulp furnish, and specified tear resistance and fold endurance. A **neutral sized** paper does not in itself qualify for the epithet of permanent paper.

permissions Permission given to a publisher for him to reproduce material which is someone else's copyright. Normally the subject of a fee.

peroxide Abbreviation for hydrogen peroxide, widely used for the bleaching of pulp (and especially mechanical pulp).

phloroglucinol Chemical used on paper to test for woodfree or mechanical furnish. Phloroglucinol is applied to a paper: if the stain remains yellow it is woodfree; if the stain turns red it contains mechanical pulp. The depth of colour of the red stain indicates the percentage of mechanical fibre present.

photocomposition Typesetting performed by a photosetter.

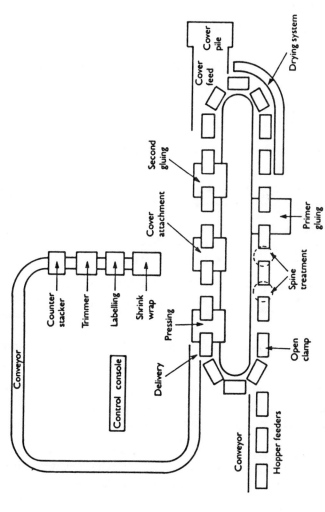

Illus 56. The perfect binding processes.

photocopy 1. Duplicate of a photograph. 2. Duplicate of a document, etc. produced on a copying machine.

photodiode A **diode** (q.v.) whose conductivity varies with the intensity of the light falling on it. Used in scanning technology. See also **CCD**, **charge coupled device**, a form of photodiode.

photoengraving Letterpress printing plate.

photogram Print made by the exposure of an object directly on photographic paper.

photogravure Gravure printing in which the cylinder image is photographically produced.

photolettering Method of setting display sized type from photographic founts.

photolithography Lithographic process with photographically produced plate image.

photomechanical Assembled type and/or illustrations as film ready for platemaking or further processing.

photomechanical transfer Abbreviated to **PMT**. Paper negative which produces a positive print by a process of chemical transfer. Extensively used for line artwork and **screened prints**.

photomontage Print comprising several other photographs.

Photon Proprietary name for a second-generation photosetter once in wide use.

photonics The use of light to transmit signals (as in **fibre optics** technology).

photopaque Opaquing fluid used to **spot** negatives.

photopolymer Plate coating which polymerises (solidifies and hardens) on exposure to strong light. Used for long runs.

photopolymer plate Letterpress printing plate made with **photopolymer** material which hardens on exposure to light. Photopolymer plates are used extensively for massmarket paperback printing.

photoprint Photographic print.

photoproof Phototypeset proof.

photoscum See **scum**.

photosetter Phototypesetting machine.

photosetting See **phototypesetting.**

photostat Trade name for a photocopy.

phototypesetting Setting type on to photographic paper or film. **Phototypesetters** employ various techniques to create the image, with computers assisting in the operational logic.

photounit The part of a phototypesetter in which the photographic image is created and exposed.

pH value Measure of acidity or alkalinity of a substance. 7=neutral; less than 7=progressive acidity; more than 7=progressive alkalinity. See **acidity.**

pic Abbreviation for **picture.** Plural: **pix.**

pica 1. Unit of typographic measurement equal to 12 points or 4.218mm (0.166044"). 2. Size of typewriter face with 10 characters to the inch.

pi characters Special characters outside the normal alphabetic range and not normally contained in a standard fount, e.g. special maths symbols.

θωερτψυιοπэ;λκφηγφδσαζξχϖβνμ

Illus 57. Some of the special characters in a pi fount.

pick-away See **pull-away.**

picking The lifting of areas of paper or coating surface during printing which happens when ink tack is stronger than the surface strength of the stock. Associated especially with coated papers, where small areas of coating come free from the body stock due to localised bonding failures between the coating mix and the body stock.

picosecond One-million-millionth of a second. Measurement of computer processing speed. Compare **millisecond, microsecond, nanosecond.**

PICT One of a number of formats in which illustration files can be held for transfer. Closely associated with the AppleMac environment.

pictogram A stylised picture which is used as a symbol. Also called a **pictograph.**

picture element See **pixel.**

picture list List of illustrations intended for a book drawn up by a picture researcher.

picture research The process of locating illustrations for a book from picture libraries, museums, galleries, etc.

pie Jumbled type. Sometimes spelt **pi**.

piece fractions Fractions built up typographically out of more than one piece of type.

pie chart A graphic diagram representing a pie, the portions of which vary to indicate values or percentages.

piggyback form A continuous stationery tractor fed carrier designed to feed headed stationery and envelopes into a printer.

pigment The constituent of a printing ink that gives it its colour.

pigmented paper Size-press coated (q.v.). or **light coated** paper.

pigment foil Foil (q.v.) which is of coloured pigment rather than imitation gold or silver.

pigskin Tough and durable book covering material made from the hide of a pig.

pile shift Device for raising or lowering the pile of stock in a press feeder or delivery.

piling See **fluffing**.

PILOT A computer language designed for computer-assisted learning applications.

pin feed The method of feeding continuous stationery by lining up pins on the machines with a series of small holes in the paper.

pin feed platen A printer cylinder that feeds paper through the machine via sprocket holes.

pinholes 1. Small holes in paper surface. 2. Small holes in the dense black image area of a negative which let through the light, and need to be **spotted out** (q.v.) using an opaquing fluid.

pin register system The use of holes and pins to provide a system of aligning copy, film and plates in register. The Protocol system is one of the best known. Also **punch register system**.

piping 1. In paper, the formation of ridges in a reel of paper left standing without a waterproof wrapper as the paper takes in or gives out moisture. 2. In film **laminating**, the formation of hard tubes on the surface of the laminate, typically caused by laminating over an ink film which is not perfectly dry.

pitch The horizontal spacing of printer characters. Common pitches are 10, 12, and 15 (10, 12 or 15 characters to the linear inch).

pitch edge The edge of the sheet which is fed into a printing or folding machine. Also known as the **gripper edge** or **leading edge**.

pixel From PICture ELements; the minute individual image/non-image areas created by the digitisation of type or graphics. A pixel is the smallest dot or element of a displayed image that can be displayed and addressed. Also **pel**.

pixel editing The ability to examine and delete individual pixels, typically around the outside of images, in order to tidy up outlines. Available on high-level **epc** systems. Also called **close cropping**.

PL/1 An early structured programming language, devised in the mid-1960s by IBM, and containing many of the features of **FORTRAN**, **ALGOL** and **COBOL**.

plain ASCII In text processing, a file which is purely words and spaces in ASCII format, stripped of all printer control codes and other word-processor codes. Such a file is ideal for text transfer.

planer Block of wood used to tap letterpress type into place on the surface of the stone.

planning All the processes involved in imposition, laying pages down on to foils in imposition sequence, etc, ready for platemaking.

planographic printing Printing from a flat (as distinct from indented or relief) image, e.g. litho.

plastic laminate proof See **plastic proof**.

plastic plate Letterpress printing plate made of plastic.

plastic proof Proof such as Cromalin, Matchprint, etc. made by exposing colour separations to a special material which images in the process colours corresponding to each separation. Also called a **dry proof**. As distinct from a **machine proof** (**wet proof**) which is made by printing from plates.

plastics Synthetic materials consisting of polymers and made from synthetic **resins** (q.v.).

plastic wrapping Wrapping magazines in polythene, usually by machine.

plate 1. A one-piece printing surface. 2. Single leaf printed on separate paper and attached to a book.

plate cylinder The press cylinder which carries the plate.

plate dampers On a litho press, the final rollers which convey the **fountain solution** to the printing plate. See also **dampening system**.

plate etch A solution applied to a litho plate to desensitise the non-image areas. Gum arabic is a common ingredient in this.

plate finish High, calendered finish given to paper.

plate folder See **buckle folder**.

plate hooked and guarded Printed **plate** fixed into a book by extending the back margin under a signature and sewing it in.

plate inkers The rollers at the bottom of the ink pyramid on a litho press which finally transfer the ink film to the plate. See also **inking system**.

platen Small letterpress printing machine on which the paper is pressed up against the vertically-held type-bed.

plate projection system A plate exposure system which works by projecting the image from microfilm or roll film rather than by the same-size one-to-one contact printing of films.

plate scanning The electronic scanning of a press-ready plate to generate a magnetic file which can be used to set the printing machine ink keys for **make-ready**. See also **CCI**.

plate section A signature or **section** of printed illustrations separated from the text matter and normally printed on a different paper, often glossy art.

plate size A size of negative or photographic print 8" x 6".

plates joined on the guard Two printed plates joined by adhesive at the back margin to form a four-page section.

platesunk Area of paper compressed (for display purposes) below the surrounding surface by a forcing plate.

plotter Device which draws graphics from computer instructions using either laser techniques or mechanical techniques. See **image setter**.

plucking See **picking.**

plug compatibility Pertaining to the manufacture of equipment that can be connected to that produced by other manufacturers via cable and plug. A form of connection commonly employed in IBM PC and compatible microcomputers.

ply Layer of paper or board joined to another for strength, thus: 2-ply, 3-ply, etc.

PM Paper machine.

PMS **Pantone Matching System.** See **Pantone.**

PMT See **photomechanical transfer.**

pocket portable A portable microcomputer developed from, and in general terms little more use than, a pocket calculator.

pointing device Generic term for a **mouse, puck** or **light-pen**: a device which controls the cursor movements on a VDU screen.

pointlining Beard on typefounders' type.

point-of-sale Place where a product is sold. e.g. a shop. **Point-of-sale material** refers to the publicity or display items used at the point of sale. Abbreviated **PoS.**

point system The main system of typographic measurement. 1pt = 0.351mm (0.013837"). See also **didot, pica.** See conversion table overleaf.

point-to-point service In telecommunications, an alternative term for a leased line (private circuit).

poke A high-level language instruction designed to place a value into a specific memory location.

polyester A plastic synthetic resin (polymers of esters). Similar in stability and toughness to **acetate,** but more flexible. Used as a stable overlay material and as a photographic film base. Trade name **mylar** (US).

polymerisation The chemical formation of **polymers**: the principle involved in the drying of ink by ultra-violet light curing, and the hardening of **photopolymer plate** material when exposed to light.

polymers Natural or synthetic plastic-like substances made up of giant molecules formed from smaller molecules of the same substances but transformed.

Conversion Table Anglo American/Didot

Anglo-American

Point size	Inches	Millimetres
1	·013837	·351
3	·041511	1·054
6	·083022	2·109
7	·096859	2·460
8	·110696	2·812
9	·124533	3·163
10	·138370	3·515
11	·152207	3·866
12	·166044	4·218
14	·193718	4·920
18	·249066	6·326
24	·332088	8·435

Didot

	Inches	Millimetres
1	·0148	·376
3	·0444	1·128
6	·0888	2·256
7	·1036	2·631
8	·1184	3·007
9	·1332	3·383
10	·1480	3·759
11	·1628	4·135
12	·1776	4·511
14	·2072	5·263
18	·2664	6·767
24	·3552	9·022

Illus 58. Point system conversion tables.

polypropylene Plastic film rather like clear polythene. In its **oriented** form, the most common material for film lamination.

polythene (polyethylene) A plastic synthetic derived ultimately from petroleum (polymerised ethylene). In low-density form it is flexible; in high-density form it is rigid.

polythene wrapping See **plastic wrapping**.

polyvinyl acetate PVA A flexible cold-melt adhesive, widely used in book binding.See under **PVA**.

polyvinyl chloride PVC A plastic synthetic derived from petroleum, mainly used as a waterproofing coating. See under **PVC**.

pop-up menu See **pull-down menu**.

pop-ups Cardboard cut-outs which stand erect.

porosity The degree to which a paper is porous to air. Porous papers very often give difficulties with feeding.

port An input and/or output connection to or from a computer.

portability In software terms, the design of programs that allows them to be run on more than one computer system. An identical name is no guarantee of portability. **BASIC**, for example, has many dialects, few of which are truly portable.

portable microcomputer A microcomputer which has all its constituent parts (processor, disc drives, keyboards, display and power source) in a single enclosure and weighs less than 30lbs.

portrait The shape of an image or page with the shorter dimension at the head and foot, as distinct from **landscape (oblong)**.

PoS Point of sale. Promotional materials such as posters, counter talkers, etc which can be displayed at any retail location where sales are carried out.

positive An image on film or paper in which the dark and light values are the same as the original, as distinct from **negative**.

positive-working plates Litho plates which are exposed using positives.

poster A single sheet in a large size printed on one side only for public display.

poster paper One-sided glazed paper with rough underside suitable for pasting.

poster type See **woodtype**.

PostScript Adobe's proprietary **page description language**. First achieved prominence through its adoption by Apple, and now the most widely used PDL supported either internally or through an external PostScript **RIP** by a broad range of laser printers and imagesetters.

PostScript fount A fount specially written in PostScript code which can be used in a PostScript-compatible printer or imagesetter.

PostScript interpreter A piece of software custom-written to convert PostScript files to a different code command set supported by a non-PostScript output device.

pot The container for molten metal on a typecasting machine.

powdering Build-up of paper dust on a litho blanket.

powderless etching Method of etching letterpress line plates in one step.

power pack The component which supplies (and controls) electrical current to other computer components.

pp Pages.

PPA Periodical Publishers Association.

ppc Printed paper case. A common finish for hardback children's books, in which the covering material over the boards is printed (and laminated) paper.

ppi Pages per inch. American method of specifying the thickness of paper.

ppm Pages per minute (laserprinting). Standard rates vary from 8-20 ppm for most of the commonly used laserprinters.

precision cutting Sheeting paper to very fine tolerances to avoid further guillotining.

precision register quoins Quoins on which the degree of adjustment can be set precisely.

preface Formal statement before the text of a book by the author. As distinct from **foreword** (q.v.).

preferred position Advertisement location which an advertiser would prefer for his copy if it is available.

prekissing Paper and blanket making contact too early, resulting in a double impression.

prelims Abbreviation of **preliminary matter**. The matter in a book which precedes the text.

Normal order of prelims

a. Half title page
b. Advertisement
c. Title page
d. Copyright page
e. Dedication
f. Acknowledgements
g. Contents list
h. List of illustrations
i. List of abbreviations
j. Foreword
k. Preface
l. Introduction

Illus 59. The normal order of prelim pages.

pre-press costs All the costs associated with bringing a job ready for press up to but not including printing the first copy. As distinct from **press costs**.

pre-press proofs Proofs made by techniques other than printing.

pre-print Previously printed matter which is then re-wound ready for running in with another printed job. Often colour advertising intended for running in with black and white newspaper work.

preprinted Part of a job printed before the main run through the press.

presensitised plate Offset litho plate supplied by the manufacturer with a light sensitive coating e.g. an offset litho plate. Often shortened to **presen plate**.

press 1. Generic term for all periodicals. 2. Printing machine.

press after correction Instruction to proceed to printing after final corrections.

press costs The costs associated with printing and manufacturing a job from plates onwards. As distinct from **pre-press costs**.

pressing Flattening folded sections before binding. Also **nipping, smashing**.

presspahn hollow A **hollow** (q.v.) made of a strip of brown reinforced card applied to the inside of the spine of a cased book. Less rigid than a **board hollow**, more durable than paper.

press proof Proof taken from the press after make-ready but before the full run.

press release News of an event sent to the press for publication.

press section In paper-making, the section of the paper-machine where the web of paper is first pressed before it is passed on to the drying cylinders.

pressure-sensitive Adhesive when pressure is applied.

preventive maintenance A regular inspection, repair and replacement routine designed to reduce the risk of system failure.

preview screen A desktop publishing VDU which allows a piece of composed work to be viewed exactly as it will appear in print. See **soft typesetter**.

primary (subtractive) colours Yellow, magenta, and cyan which, with black, make up the four process colours.

primer Print working which acts as a base or undercoat for a colour which will otherwise lack covering power, e.g. a metallic silver or gold ink.

print 1. A photograph. 2. A common operating system command to print a specified file list.

print control character A non-printing character designed to perform an action such as line feed or carriage return.

print drum A rotating drum containing printable characters. See **drum printer**.

printed circuit board A plastic base with a copper coating on to which electronic components are attached. Unwanted areas of copper are removed by acid etching.

printed paper case See **ppc**.

printed waste Printed paper used as a furnish for recycling.

print engine In a laser printer, that mechanical part that performs the physical printing function. As distinct from the **RIP** (q.v.).

printer A peripheral designed to produce a hard copy of text or simple graphics characters. Characters may be printed as fully-formed characters (see **daisywheel printer**, **drum printer**) or made up from a series of dots (see **dot matrix printer**, **ink jet printer**, **laser printer**).

printer driver See **driver**.

printer's devil Apprentice in a printing shop.

printer's error See **PE**.

printing cylinder See **plate cylinder**.

printing down Laying film over a light-sensitive plate or paper to produce an image.

printings Papers suitable for printing.

printing sequence The order in which the four process colours are applied.

printmaking Making fine art reproductions of originals.

print-out The text printed out by a computer printer.

print-out mask See **burn-out mask**.

print to paper Instruction to the printer to use all available paper for a job, rather than printing to a specific quantity of copies.

print wheel See **daisywheel**.

process blue, red, yellow Used to indicate the cyan, magenta and yellow colours of the four-colour **process inks**.

process camera Camera designed for the various photographic processes involved in printing, as distinct from original photography.

process colour See **four-colour process**.

process engraving Letterpress engraving.

process inks Cyan, magenta, yellow and black formulated as a **set** of four to print colour.

process lens Photographic lens designed for graphic arts work.

process plates Half-tone colour plates for four-colour process printing.

process set The four process inks.

process white Also, **Chinese white**. Specially pure white paint which can be used for correcting camera-ready illustrations.

pro-forma invoice Invoice drawn up to show the value of goods, and needed either for documentation purposes or to obtain pre-payment.

program The complete set of instructions which control a computer in the performance of a task.

program counter The register that contains the address of the next program instruction to be executed.

program library A suite of general purpose computer programs held on backing store.

programmable Any device that can receive, store and act on a computer program.

programmer The person employed to write, develop or maintain computer programs.

programming A sequential list of instructions by which a computer performs its designated tasks. Programs may be written in one of many **high-level languages (BASIC, Pascal, FORTH, COBOL**, (etc.) or a **low-level language** (q.v.). High-level languages are often suitable for amateur or hobby use while low-level languages would almost certainly only be used by professional programmers.

progressive proofs or **progressives** or **progs** Proofs of each plate in a colour set showing each colour alone and in combination with the others as a guide to colour matching, at the printing stage. Se also **bastard progressives.**

projection platemaking equipment Equipment such as the Rachwal or DaiNippon systems which make plates by exposing from 35mm or 70mm roll microfilms mounted in the head of computer-controlled step-and-project machines. The microfilm contains the pages of the job shot sequentially; the step-and-project machine is programmed to locate and expose each page in imposition order on to the plate.

PROLOG An acronym for PROgramming in LOGic languages. PROLOG has been developed for use in artificial intelligence applications and has been adopted by the Japanese as the main language for their fifth-generation computers.

PROM Programmable Read Only Memory. Stored programs which cannot be altered by the user. See also **firmware.**

PROM burner See **PROM programmer.**

PROM progammer A device designed to write data to a PROM chip.

prompt A message, usually displayed but sometimes audible, requesting an action from a computer user.

proof A trial printed sheet or copy, made before the production run, for the purpose of checking.

proof-reader's marks Symbols used by a proof-reader in marking corrections on proofs.

proof-reading Checking typeset proofs for accuracy.

proportional spacing Pertaining to attempts to approach typeset quality in word processor output by assigning different spacing values to printable characters.

proprietary software Manufacturers' off-the-shelf software packages such as WordStar, Lotus 1-2-3, dBase, etc.

protective ground Electrical connection between two electronic devices designed to prevent damage to either. Protective ground is typically provided in an **RS232C** interface via pin 1.

Protext Page make-up system marketed by Interset.

protocol The whole formal set of codes and conventions which are employed by a computer system to control its internal communications, and which also define its communications with other systems. As far as protocols for representing text are concerned, the main schemes are **ASCII** in microcomputers; **TTS** in many Linotype machines; **EBCDIC** in IBM mini and mainframe computers; etc. Other protocols involve the formats used as data transfer proceeds (serial or parallel), the pace at which the transfer proceeds (baud rate), and the system set-ups designed at each end for despatch and receipt. See under **data transmission**.

protocol converter Any device which is capable of receiving data in one form and outputting it in another, so establishing communication between devices employing different protocols. A **media converter** is an example of a sophisticated form of protocol converter.

prove To pull a proof.

provincial press Newspapers circulating in regional areas.

PS/2 IBM's own Personal System/2 family of computers.

PSTN Public Switched Telephone Network The normal telephone lines as distinct from special leased or **dedicated** lines. Leased lines generally offer the possibility of higher data transmission speeds and lower error rates.

psychrometer Instrument used for determining **relative humidity RH**.

PT Precision trimmed (paper).

PTR Acronym for **paper tape reader**.

public domain Material which is free from copyright encumbrance and freely available to anyone who wishes to use it.

publisher's statement Publisher's authorised notice of circulation and distribution statistics.

puck A pointing device with functions similar to cursor keys or a **mouse**. It does not generally have the same degree of freedom of movement as a mouse but rather works within a tray-like enclosure.

pull 1. A proof. 2. A single print for subsequent photo-litho reproduction, often called a **repro pull**.

pull-away A section which contains a number of blank pages (typically 4pp) either in the middle or at front and back, which are to be removed prior to binding. Also, **pick-away**.

pull down menus Also referred to as **pop-up menus**. Options are revealed only when a menu type is accessed, usually by a pointing and dragging action with a **mouse**. Once the option has been selected the menu disappears leaving the screen free.

pulling Resistance between paper and printing surface.

pull-out Part of a publication which can be removed from the binding and used separately.

pullquote Extract, or extracted text (US).

pulp The raw suspension of woodfibre, treated either chemically or mechanically, in water. **Chemical pulp** contains many fewer impurities than **mechanical pulp** (q.v.).

pulp board A **homogenous** board manufactured to its full thickness on the papermaking machine.

pulpwood Wood for the manufacture of wood pulp.

punch binding See **burst binding**.

punched card Card punched with a pattern of holes encoding data for subsequent reading.

punched tape See **paper tape**.

punch register system Device which punches registered holes in sets of films or plates for positioning puposes. Also, **pin register system**.

pure woodfree See **woodfree**.

PVA polyvinyl acetate A water-based **cold-melt** emulsion adhesive made from synthetic resins. It has low initial tack but good penetration and excellent flexibility. In binding it is widely used for perfect binding (especially in conjuction with **hot-melt** adhesive as a two-shot process); for spine gluing in sewn work; for tipping on endpapers; and for casing in. It needs forced drying methods. Compare **hot-melt adhesive, starch paste, animal glue.**

PVC polyvinyl chloride In bookbinding materials and similar, a liquid plastic used for coating or for impregnation into base paper for waterproofing and durability.

Q

QA Quality assurance In management, the imposition of systematic techniques to ensure that all work is produced to measured and consistent standards, pre-empting quality control problems.

QC Quality control In manufacturing, the checking and monitoring procedures necessary to control the quality of output.

quad 1. Paper terminology for a sheet four times the size of the traditional **broadside** sheet e.g. 'Quad Demy', 890 x 1130 mm. 2. Letterpress spacing material used to fill out lines of type.

quad left, right or centre To set lines flush left, right or centre.

quad press Printing press designed for a maximum sheet approximately 1010 x 1400 mm (40" x 56"), ie. a '**quad**' sheet.

quadretone Proprietary process for descreening and rescreening colour separation films with a minimum loss of quality when they are needed at a new size.

quadrille Grid paper.

qualified 1. Reader who meets criteria necessary to receive free subscription of periodical. 2. Research subject who meets the criteria being tested by the project.

quality In paper, the brand or type of paper. Also called **grade**.

quality control System for checking quality of products during or after manufacture.

Quark XPress One of several pre-eminent page make-up systems for the AppleMac. See also **PageMaker, Ready, Set, Go!**.

quarter-bound Binding with spine in one material (e.g. leather) and sides in another (e.g. cloth.) Compare **fullbound, half-bound, three-quarter bound**.

quarter tone Illustration made by retouching a coarse-screen halftone print to emphasise the shadows by making them solid and the highlights by making them white, following which the illustration is reshot as fine line.

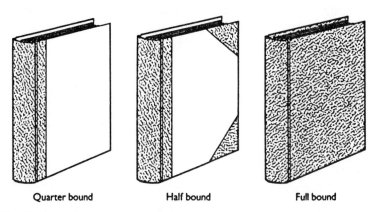

Quarter bound   Half bound   Full bound

Illus 60. Quarter-bound, half-bound and fullbound binding styles.

quarto A page one-quarter of the traditional **broadside** sheet size, e.g. Crown Quarto.

quire 1. One-twentieth of a ream (25 sheets). 2. Section or signature.

quirewise binding Saddle stitching.

quoin A wedge or expanding device used to lock up letterpress chases.

quotes Quotation marks, inverted commas.

qwerty Standard typewriter keyboard layout, qwerty being the arrangement of keys on the top left hand row of the board.

R

rack board Display board or device designed to be mounted on a rack.

radio-frequency drying Drying by the use of radio-frequency waves (more familiarly known as microwaves). Used for drying adhesives in some book-binding lines.

ragged right Text with irregular line lengths, i.e. with an even left margin but an uneven right margin.

rag paper Paper made from stock containing a substantial percentage of rag.

rail Part of a linecasting machine. Terms 'upper rail' and 'lower rail' are sometimes used by extension to denote shift and unshift.

raised printing See **thermographic printing**.

RAM Random access memory. RAM is the temporary, interactive, area of memory in a computer in which programs work and manipulate the data. Data in RAM is lost when the computer is switched off unless it is first saved to disc. Compare **ROM**.

RAM cache A form of **RAM disc** which is powered by an independent small battery inside the computer, and which, unlike a normal RAM disc, therefore retains its contents after the computer is switched off. Also **hard RAM**.

RAM disc A large area of RAM memory that holds some or all of the contents of a floppy or hard disc enabling far faster read-write operations. At the end of a session the contents of a RAM disc are rewritten back to floppy or hard disc. See also **hard RAM, RAM cache**.

ram stacker Heavy-duty bundling machine which condenses stacks of web-offset printed sections ready for binding.

r&b or **r&j** See **rounding and backing, rounding and jointing**.

R&D Research and development.

random access Method of directly accessing a specific address on a computer file without the need for a sequential process. **Random access memory** is often abbreviated to **RAM** (q.v.).

range Align (type, etc.).

ranging figs Arabic numerals that are of equal height. Otherwise called **lining figs**, or **modern figs**.

rapid access processing Method of quick film and paper processing using heated chemicals. **Rapid access paper** is the photographic material used. See also **stabilization** paper.

raster In laser setting, the underlying pattern or 'net' of lines which represents the structure over which the 'typeset' image is formed by the selective exposure of dots in a series of horizontal, line-by-line, sweeps.

raster data Data held in raster, or **bitmap**, form. Contrast **vector data**, which is much more economical in storage than bitmap data.

raster image processor (RIP) Device used in area make-up systems which processes front end system commands relating to individual lots of type and images and instructs a laser output device to arrange and output the type and images together in their correct positions.

raster scanning The technique of reading or plotting an image by the selective identification or **sampling** of dots, line by line, in a series of horizontal sweeps following a **raster** pattern or grid.

rate card Leaflet or kit showing costs of advertisement space in a publication.

raw data Data before processing or preparation.

raw stock Base paper before coating.

RCF Acronym for **recycled fibre**: secondary fibre from retree, broke or other paper waste as opposed to virgin fibre from trees.

reader 1. Person who checks proofs for accuracy. 2. Device which can 'read' from magnetic media or, in the case of OCR, from typescript.

readership Number of readers of a publication, as distinct from the number of copies sold. See **pass-on rate**.

reader's proof First **galley** proof used by the printer's reader.

read-only memory See **ROM**.

read-write head The component which reads from and writes to a magnetic disc or tape.

Ready,Set,Go! Along with its main rivals **Pagemaker** and **Quark XPress**, an interactive wysiwyg page make-up system for the AppleMac.

ready state An indication in a **DTE/DCE** interface that the DTE device is ready to receive incoming data and the DCE device is ready to accept a request to send data.

real time Method of computing in which operations are performed on data simultaneously with input and output.

ream Five hundred sheets of paper.

ream-wrapped Sheets wrapped in lots of 500.

rebind Binding a set of stored sheets, set aside after the first binding.

recall Calling a computer file from backing store into memory.

reciprocating roller On a printing press, the roller in a dampening or inking system which moves laterally from time to time across the width of the other rollers to distribute the solution or ink more evenly.

recognition memory In an OCR device, the read-only memory (ROM) which holds the pattern characteristics of the particular range of founts which the machine is programmed to read. See **optical character recognition**.

reconstituted leather Leather made from pulp of different leather scraps.

record A discrete block of computer data, typically consisting of a number of **fields** (q.v.).

recorder or **recording unit** See **imagesetter**.

Recover An operating system command used to recover damaged or deleted disc files. When a file is deleted, only its reference in the disc index is removed. Provided the user has not attempted to write new data to the disc, the Recover command may be used to resurrect such files.

recovered fibres Fibres from waste paper as opposed to virgin pulp. Also, **secondary fibres, recycled fibres**.

recto A right-hand page.

recycled fibres See **recovered fibres**.

reducers Printing ink additives.

redundancy In computing, the duplication of a system or part of a system such that if one part fails the duplicate takes over. No data is lost and no production time is lost.

reel Roll of paper. Also, **web**.

reel-stand The unit housing a reel of paper at the feed end of a web-offset press. Multi-colour, multi-effect, web-offset machines may have up to three reel-stands feeding paper simultaneously. The printed webs are brought together in the folder, and are folded together.

reel up The reeling section of a paper machine.

re-etch To deepen the image on a plate.

refiner mechanical pulp RMP Pulp made by passing wood chips through a refiner. Midway in quality between **stone groundwood mechanical pulp (SGW)** and **thermomechanical pulp (TMP)**.

refining The second main stage of papermaking after dry pulp has been mixed in a **hydrapulper** at the first stage. The stock from the hydrapulper is further refined in a **cone refiner** and, after cleaning, is ready for pumping to the paper machine. Also known as **beating**.

reflection copy Copy viewed by its reflected light, e.g. a photograph, as distinct from **transmission copy** (q.v.), which is viewed by transmitted light. Also known as **reflective copy**, and **reflex** copy.

reformatting Setting new typographical parameters for a previously set piece of copy.

refresh rate Rate at which an apparently continuously displayed image is flashed on a VDT, e.g. 60 times a second, etc.

refusal When one ink film will not print on another.

register 1. Positioning of colours accurately to form a composite image. 2. Storage location in computer memory.

register marks Marks in the same relative position on films or plates to enable correct positioning to be achieved.

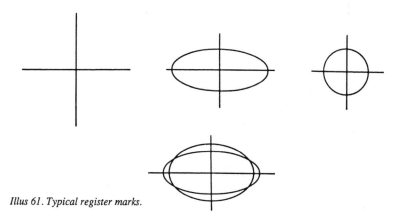

Illus 61. Typical register marks.

register pins Pins which locate in holes made by a punch in a **punch register** system (q.v.).

register punch See **punch register**.

re-issue A publication which has been out of print and is then re-published either by the original publisher or by a new publisher.

relative humidity (RH) The amount of water vapour present in the atmosphere at a given temperature expressed as a percentage of saturation at that temperature. Standard testing conditions for paper are 23 degrees C and 50%RH. Optimum press conditions are 20 degrees C and 55-65%RH.

relative units Divisions of one em used as a fine measurement for spacing or character-width calculations.

release Amendment made to a **version** (major edition) of software.

relief Printing method using a raised image, e.g. letterpress.

remainders Unsold books which are discounted for sale on preferential terms. Primarily used in relation to books.

remote Located away from main plant or, in the case of technical equipment, having no direct electronic link with the main processing plant.

remote diagnostics The checking and rectification of a computer program or database by remote access through a telephone link rather than by attendance on site.

removable cartridge disc A disc system in which hard discs, contained within protective cartridges, may be removed from and replaced in suitable disc drives. Also **removable disc pack**.

Rename A command common to several operating systems, which enables the user to change the name of a file.

renewal Repeat of subscription to a periodical.

repeat 1.Repeated insertion or showing of an advertisement. 2. In printing, a faint image outline seen in printed work (usually in solid areas) which is caused by poor ink film recovery on the plate rollers – **ink starvation**. Similar in appearance to **ghosting** (q.v.), and often confused with it.

repeater See **Cambridge ring**.

replacement fee Fee paid to a picture library to cover the cost of replacing a lost or spoiled picture.

repp Writing paper with a patterned surface.

reprint 1. Subsequent printing of the first edition of a publication. 2. Printing of part of a publication for promotional or editorial use.

repro All the stages of pre-press camerawork, scanning and film make-up which go on from the time that the first **originals** for a job are submitted to the time that plate-ready films for printing are prepared. Also, **origination**.

reproduction See **repro**.

reproduction fee Fee paid for the right to reproduce an illustration.

reproduction proof A proof taken from type for subsequent reproduction.

reprographics or **reprography** General term for electrostatic printing, diazo printing, or any other form of short-run duplicating and printing.

repro paper Coated paper suitable for use in camera-ready artwork. Also called **baryta paper**.

reproportion Change in the relative dimensions of artwork (usually photographically) to create a new shape.

repro pull See **reproduction proof**.

Request To Send (RTS) A signal sent by a transmitting device indicating that it is ready to transmit data. Compare **Clear To Send**. See **handshake**.

rescreen To take a subject which is already screened (e.g. a printed photograph) and shoot it again with a new half-tone screen. It is important in doing this to avoid moiré patterning (q.v.).

resident fount In laser printers, a fount which is supplied by the manufacturer. Also, **internal fount**.

residual coating Very fine layer of surface coating left by incomplete processing in the non-image area of a litho plate, and which will cause **scum** when the plate is printed.

resiliency Measure of paper surface condition after printing.

resin coated paper Abbreviated to **RC paper**. Photographic paper with good longevity of image used in photosetting.

resins Viscous, sticky organic substances exuded from trees. Soluble in alcohol and used as varnishes. Natural resins are rosin and shellac. **Synthetic resins** are natural resins which have been chemically modified (polymerised): examples are **polythene**, **PVC**, and **polypropylene**.

resist A protective chemical or coating.

resolution Measurement of image fineness stated in lines per inch (**lpi**), dots per inch (**dpi**), or pixels per inch as created by an output device such as a scanner, imagesetter, laser typesetter, or laser printer. Low-resolution laser printers output typically at 300 dpi, medium-resolution at 400 dpi, high resolution at 600 dpi. Laser photosetters output typically at around 1200 dpi (medium) up to 2400 dpi (high). Some imagesetters output at lower resolutions vertically than horizontally (1600H x 800V for example). VDU screen resolutions typically vary from 72-100 pixels (dots) per inch.

response time The time taken to access and then display the result of a command on a VDU.

Restore An operating system command to restore to a fixed disc a file or group of files that have been stored on floppy disc by a **backup** operation.

retarders Printing ink solvents which extend the ink's **open time** (q.v.) on press.

reticulation The drawing together of an ink into a pattern of fine beads, often caused when a wet film of ink is printed on to a previously printed ink film which has dried to a smooth glossy finish.

retouching Correcting a photographic print or transparency before reproduction. As applied to colour separation films, see colour **etching**.

retree Slightly damaged paper sold at a reduced price and often marked **xx.** See also **broke**.

returns Unsold stocks returned by a bookseller with the publisher's prior agreement.

reversal Creation of white text or images on a black background. Sometimes referred to as **WOB** (white on black). See **reverse out**.

reversal film Contact film with the same positive and negative values as the original, i.e. black is reproduced as black. Also, **autopositive film, direct duplicating film**.

reversed out Type printing white out of another colour.

reverse indent See **hanging indent**.

reverse leading Ability of a photosetter to move film or paper 'backwards' to achieve exposure of columnar matter.

reverse-reading See **wrong-reading**.

reverse video An ability provided by some systems to reverse the VDU image so that data is displayed as black characters on a white (or green or amber) background. Also known as **inverse video**.

review copy A copy of a book sent to a newspaper or magazine for reviewing.

review slip Enclosure slip sent with a review copy describing the book and giving its publication details.

revise A revised proof for subsequent reading.

RGB Red, green, blue. The three primary colours of light which together make up the spectrum of white light; and the colours of the three electron guns in a **colour monitor** (q.v.).

RH Relative humidity (q.v.).

ribbon cable Flat plastic coated cable in which the lines lie parallel to each other.

ribbon folder Web press folder which cuts web into ribbons for folding. As distinct from a **former folder** (q.v.).

RIFF Acronym for **Raster Image File Format**. A computer file format for the description of high-resolution bitmaps such as photographs. Similar to the more widely used **TIFF** format (q.v.).

right-angle folding Folding a sheet with one or more folds at right-angles to each other.

right-angle folds Folds at 90 degree angles to each other.

right-grain Refers to a book in which the grain of the paper is correct, ie running parallel to the spine of the book from head to tail. The opposite is **cross-grain** (q.v.), or **wrong-grain**.

right-reading Film which reads 'correctly', i.e., from left to right, when viewed from the emulsion side. As distinct from **wrong-reading** (q.v.).

rights See **subsidiary rights**.

right side In paper-making, the **top side** or **felt-side** of the web (q.v.).

rigid disc See **hard disc.**

ring binding Binding by means of holes in paper which locate on metal rings.

RIP 1. Rest In Proportion. An instruction to allow al the other pieces in a batch of artwork to undergo the same enlargement or reduction as one piece marked. 2. See **raster image processor.**

risc technology Reduced instruction set coding: techniques in computing to reduce the amount of coding and so interpreting necessary inside a computer by using more 'hard-wired' microcircuitry, so increasing processing speeds.

river Undesirable formation of word spaces into a vertical 'river' of white in the text.

RMP See **refiner mechanical pulp** (q.v.).

rocker sealer Heated element in film wrapping machine which seals centre join.

Roland Proprietary name for the wide series of litho colour presses manufactured by MAN-Roland.

roll Reel (US usage).

roll coating Coating applied to paper by rollers.

rolled Paper glazed by rolling.

rolling ball See **tracker ball.**

roll-out Using a roller to spread ink on paper for sampling purposes.

roll wrapping Rolling a magazine to wrap paper around it for mailing (as distinct from folding).

ROM or **Read Only Memory** Computer memory supplied as a chip inside the computer and which cannot be altered by the user. ROM typically contains the basic system programs resident in the computer. Compare **RAM**, which is the interactive part of the computer's memory.

roman figures Roman numerals such as iii, xviii, xxv, etc.

roman type 'Upright' letters as distinct from **italic** (q.v.). Known as **plain** or normal in **DTP** systems.

root directory In computing, the main or 'top' directory in a hierarchical file structure.

ROP Abbreviation for 'Run of Paper'. In magazines or newspapers: material printed as part of the main text.

ro-ro Abbreviation for roll-on, roll-off: describes sea freighting by lorry where the lorry drives on to the boat with its cargo and drives off at the other end. Nothing is unloaded.

rosin Used in conjunction with **alum,** an important component in paper-making **size** (q.v.).

rotary Printing from plates on cylinders.

rotogravure Gravure printing on rotary press.

rough A sketch or layout.

rough proof Proof for identification rather than reading.

rounding and backing Also **rounding and jointing.** Shaping a book so the back is convex. As distinct from **flat back** binding.

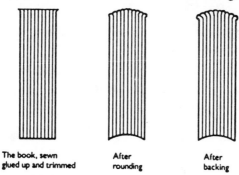

The book, sewn
glued up and trimmed

After
rounding

After
backing

Illus 62. Rounding and backing.

round-pile feeder A folding machine feeder which feeds from a rounded pile as distinct from a **flat-pile feeder** which feeds from a conventional flat pile of sheets.

routine A computer program with a selective task.

routing Cutting away non-printing areas of a plate.

royal Standard size of paper 480 x 636mm (metric system).

Royal Fount description language developed jointly by Apple and Micro-soft as an output standard for AppleMac computers. An alternative output to **PostScript** (q.v.).

royalties Payments made to an author for every book sold, usually calculated as a percentage of the published price for home sales, and as a percentage of net receipts for overseas sales.

R/P Reprinting. One of a number of standard **answers** that may be given by a publisher to a bookseller enquiring about the availability of a given book.

RS232C The standard **serial communications** socket used in data transfer.

RS422 A more robust version of the **RS232C**, specially designed for integrated technology.

RTF Acronym for **Rich Text Format**. An inter-computer file-format alternative to ASCII for the transfer of files from computer to computer, but supporting formatting information in addition to the normal transmission codes. Devised by Microsoft and supported by later versions of MacWrite and by WriteNow.

RTS See **Request to Send**.

R type Colour print made from a transparency without any intermediate negative. Contrast **C type**.

rubbing up Inking a plate image by applying the ink on a cloth with a rubbing action while the plate is moistened.

rub-down lettering See **transfer type**.

rubilith Red masking film which is opaque to light and used in making photographic **masks** for drop-outs, reverses, tint-laying, etc.

rub-out Computer code which deletes.

rub-proof Ink with good abrasion resistance.

ruby See **agate**.

rule A line (of specified thickness).

Illus 63. Common weights of rule.

rule-up sheet In imposition and planning, the basic drawn grid which establishes all the main positions for the pages and type areas within them.

run 1. The activation of a computer program. 2. Number of printed copies of a publication.

run-around Type set around a picture or other element of design.

run length encoding One of the techniques used in the **data compression** of illustration scan files. Run length encoding identifies and logs runs of 0's or 1's, so reducing the amount of data that needs to be stored or transmitted.

runnability Ability of paper to be printed without problems.

running head A title repeated at the top of each page. Also known as **running headline**.

running order 1. Set of notes indicating the order of events in a production. 2. List of the contents of a printed work to guide the printer in his imposition.

running text Normal continuous main text on a page (as distinct from displayed material).

run-of-book See **run-of-paper**.

run-of-paper Advertisement location allocated at the publisher's choice, anywhere in the publication.

run on 1. To continue a text without a paragraph or line break. 2. To continue to print copies after an initial stated print run is completed.

run-on costs The costs, normally expressed per thousand copies, of continuing to print without stopping the printing machine beyond a stated number. Thus, the costs of 5000 copies plus 1000 run-on copies.

run out Output film or bromide from a phototypesetting machine.

run through Ruled lines stretching from one edge of the paper to the other with no breaks.

RW Ream wrapped. **RWOP** is ream wrapped on pallets.

S

S100 A parallel bus standard developed for microcomputers employing 8080 microprocessors.

saddle Equipment made up of two metal plates joined together in the form of an inverted v over which the **sections** of a book or magazine are laid for either section **sewing** or for **insetting**.

saddle stitching Binding inset books with wire staples through the middle fold of the sheets. Also, **saddle wire-stitching**.

saddle thread-sewing See **Singer-sewing**.

safelight Darkroom lamp which does not affect photographic materials.

sale or return A sales arrangement which allows the buyer to return any unsold books for credit.

sample In scanning or output technology, a microscopic area of an image undergoing scanning and analysis. Also **dot, pixel**.

samples per inch See **dpi**.

sampling In scanning, the process of taking samples at fixed intervals and in a fixed and logical grid-like order.

sans serif Also, **Lineale**. A typeface with no **serifs** (q.v.).

Satstream A digital satellite communications service operated by British Telecom.

saturation The depth or intensity of colour in a subject, ie its freedom from white.

Save The operation of storing data on disc or tape.

sawn-in sewing Sewing with cuts in the backs of sections to take cords.

sc 1. Small caps. 2. **Supercalendered** (paper).

scaling Calculating or marking the enlargement or reduction of an original for reproduction.

scamp Rough layout. Also, **rough**.

scan-a-web Method of scanning the image on a moving web by means of rotating mirror.

scanner Computer controlled sampling device which reads the relative colour densities of copy and produces colour separations. See **analyse scanner, output scanner, epc system.**

scatter proofs Proofs of illustrations where the subjects are arranged in random order. As distinct from **imposed colour proofs** (q.v.).

scavenger rollers Small-diameter rollers in an ink train which pick off fluff and lint from the main rollers.

schedule 1. Sequence of events and deadlines agreed for production. 2. Schedule of bookings for an advertising campaign.

scheduler An operating system utility that initiates processes according to assigned priorities and available system resources.

SCL Scanner command language. Computer language governing the format in which images are collected, stored, and output. See also **TIFF**.

score To impress paper with a rule to ease folding.

Scotchprint Proprietary translucent proofing material used with hot-metal repro formes.

scratch pad memory A small area of memory used as a temporary working area.

screen 1. Pattern of lines that creates the dot formation in **half-tones** (q.v.) As well as the normal **crossline screen** at 45 degrees, other screens include the **vertical** screen at 90 degrees, **one-way** screen, **linen** screen, **textured** screen, **mezzotint** screen, etc. 2. See **visual display unit** (terminal).

screen angles Varied angles of each screen used in colour half-tones to avoid **moiré patterns**. The conventionl screen angles are:

black	45 degrees
magenta	75 degrees
yellow	90 degrees
cyan	105 degrees (15 degrees)

screen clash Moiré patterning caused by incorrect screen angles, or occurring when previously printed, screened, halftones are rescreened.

screen dump A print-out of the contents of a VDU screen.

screened bromide or **screened print** A print with a half-tone screen, typically a **PMT** (q.v.).

screen editor Type of text-processing program now universal in word-processing which permits the editing of text using a cursor which can be moved anywhere around the screen. As distinct from a **line editor** style of program (more associated with computer programming) which permits text-editing only at one named line at a time.

screen finder A plastic viewer placed over a half-tone to determine the screen ruling.

screen fount In **wysiwyg** screen displays, a fount which appears on screen as the actual design of character of the type which will be output.

screenless litho Printing by litho with specially coated plates that can hold continuous-tone detail.

screen make-up Page make-up using a computer screen (as in DTP and other interactive page make-up programs).

screen printing or **screen process printing** See **silk screen printing**.

screen ruling The number of lines or dots per inch on a screen. The conventional screen rulings in common use for bookwork are 100, 120, 133, 150 lines per inch (40, 48, 54, 60 lines per centimetre).

screen tint Film with dots in one of a grade of percentages (10% - 90%) used for printing a shade of a colour rather than its full strength.

scribed lines Lines scratched on the emulsion of film for subsequent printing.

script A typeface which simulates handwriting.

abcdefghijklmnopqrstuvwxyz
ABCDEFGHIJKLMNOPQRSTUVWXYZ
1234567890 .,;: "«»&!?

Illus 64. A script typeface.

scrolling Moving text vertically into and out of the display area of a VDU.

scrubbing A machine fault which results in uneven and early wear of plates and blankets.

SCSI Small Computer Standard Interface. A common interfacing standard in the AppleMac environment.

scum or **scumming** Build-up of ink on the non-image area of an offset plate, which therefore starts to print. Scumming can be caused by a number of circumstances, but often because a small amount of residual coating has been left on the plate after processing; or because of the partial **oxidation** of the plate – the formation of surface corrosion by reaction with the air.

search and replace See **global search and replace**.

search fee Fee charged by a picture service to cover the cost of conducting research in its own files on a client's behalf.

search key An item to be compared with specified areas in a database search.

search routine Computer routine for finding specified words or groups of words in text.

secondary Clear to Send A signal in an RS232C interface when used with modems providing primary and secondary transmission lines, the primary line providing a high data rate with the secondary line providing a lower data rate in the opposite direction. See **Clear to Send**.

secondary colour The colour made by a mixture of two primaries, e.g. yellow + red = orange.

secondary fibres See **recovered fibres**.

second cover Inside front cover.

second-generation computers Early computers using transistors in place of vacuum tubes.

second-generation photosetters Photosetters using electromechanical means (negative strips, engraved discs) of exposing typefounts.

second-level heading Second in number (and importance) of a series of headings in a book.

seconds See **retree**.

section A folded sheet which forms part of a book. Also called a **signature**.

section sewing Conventional sewing, as in most paperback or hardback books. The full specification is **section-sewn continuous**, or **French sewn** or **Smyth sewn** (US), (q.v.).

sector In computing, a subdivision of a **track** on a computer disc. See **disc**.

sector mapping A method of speeding up disc access time. If sector addresses are recorded sequentially the operating system will have to wait for the disc to complete a revolution before the next can be accessed. The spreading of sector addresses around the disc gives the operating system time to process each before the next reaches the read-write head.

security paper Paper incorporating features which make counterfeiting difficult.

see-safe A sales agreement that all books left unsold after a specified period can be returned for credit. Compare the **sale or return** arrangement, which accepts that books may be returned for credit after any period with no prior commitment.

see-through See **show-through**.

selected file backup A means of improving storage space on backup discs or tapes by copying data blocks sequentially. In this way unused or redundant blocks are not copied.

Selectric Composition **golfball typewriter** (q.v.) manufactured by IBM.

self-adhesive paper Carbonless copy paper.

self copy paper Carbonless copy paper.

self cover Cover of the same paper as text pages.

self-ends First and last pages of a book block used as endpapers.

self-mailer Printed piece mailed without envelope.

semi-chemical pulp Combination of chemical and mechanical pulp.

semiconductor Material used in the construction of transistors, diodes and photoelectric cells. Semiconductor devices have the property of altering their electrical resistance under given sets of circumstances, thus acting as switching devices or 'gates'.

semi-display Advertisements displayed in boxes or laid out as a full or part page within classified advertisement pages.

semi-matt A matt coated paper which is given a little extra calendering giving it a smooth and slightly glossy finish halfway between a matt and a full gloss finish.

sensitivity guide Piece of film with graded density used to monitor exposure.

separation See **colour separation, origination**.

separation negative See **colour separation negative**.

sequential access Reading items in computer memory in sequence rather than by **random access** (q.v.).

serial communication See **serial transmission**.

serial interface An interface that is only able to pass information in serial form. See **RS232C, serial transmission**.

serial printer One which prints a single character at a time. Compare **line printer, page printer**.

serial to parallel converter A device that converts the sequential input from a serial transmission device and passes it on via the required number of parallel lines.

serial transmission Data communications method in which each component **bit** of a character is transmitted in sequence down the wire, and is then reassembled with its fellows on arrival. Contrast **parallel transmission**.

series A complete range of sizes in the same typeface.

serifs The short cross lines on the ends of ascenders, descenders and strokes of letters in certain typefaces.

Illus 65. Serifs.

serigraphy See **silk screen printing**.

set 1. To typeset, output, or otherwise record an image on paper or film. Frequently used synonyms include **plot, record, output.** 2. The width of a character.

set-off The transfer of wet ink to another sheet. Typically occurs at the delivery end of the printing press. Precautions can include the use of an **anti set-off spray** (q.v.).

set solid Type set with no extra **leading** between the lines.

setting rule Brass rule used for measurement in a **composing stick** (q.v.).

set width See **set**.

sew To fasten the sections of a book with thread.

sexto Obsolete term for one-sixth of a standard size sheet.

SFL Sheetfed litho.

SGML Standard Generalised Mark-up Language. A complex **generic coding scheme** adopted as both an ISO International Standard and as a BSI British Standards Institution standard.

SGW Stone groundwood pulp (q.v.).

shade The lightness or darkness of a colour, as distinct from its **hue** (q.v.).

shaded watermark Watermark with opaque rather than transparent appearance.

shadowmask A perforated sheet at the rear of a colour CRT screen that is used to separate beams from red, green and blue electron beam guns.

shadows Dark parts in a photograph or half-tone print represented by 70%-100% dot sizes. Contrast **highlights, mid-tones**.

shank The body of a piece of type.

shantung One of a number of finishes typically offered in imitation cloths. Shantung is a light cotton-weave finish.

shared file One that can be accessed by two systems and which may be used to provide a means of communication.

sharpening image The progressive thinning out of an image as printing proceeds, to the point at worst where fine lines and highlight dots start to disappear. Its opposite is a **thickening image**.

sheet The full-size piece of paper for printing, before folding or cutting.

sheeter Machine which cuts reels to sheets.

sheet fed printing Printing by separate sheets as distinct from reels.

sheet stock Publisher's printed sections held at the printer for binding up later.

sheetwise Printing one side of a sheet at a time, as distinct from **perfecting** (q.v.).

sheetwork To print each side of the sheet from a separate forme. Each sheet yields one copy. As distinct from **work and turn** (q.v.).

shelf life The usable storage life of a material (e.g. a plate).

shelf talker PoS card advertising a book in a shop, placed on the shelf where the book is displayed.

shell In computing (and particularly in the UNIX operating environment), an alternative term for the **command processor** (q.v.).

shielded cable A data transmission communications cable that is shielded against external interference by a grounded metallic outer wrapping. See **noise**.

shift A key which, when depressed, gives a different designation to all the other keys, e.g. turns a lower case letter into upper case.

shift codes Codes employed to increase the number of addressable characters. By reserving two characters to perform shift and unshift functions the number of available characters is doubled.

shingle The allowance made in imposition for **creep** (q.v.), i.e. the fractional space by which the back margins of the outer pages of a section need to be increased in order to make all the back margins appear to be equal when the section is folded.

shive Bundles of coarse fibre in mechanical paper or pulp.

shoot Photograph.

short-cross The short axis of a sheet of paper, as distinct from the **long-cross** or long axis. In **work and turn** printing, the sheets are turned across the short-cross axis to be backed up.

short-grain Sheet of paper in which the grain is parallel to the short edge of the sheet. Compare **long-grain**.

short-grain press An A-series size of press that produces A4 in **cross-grain** (short-grain) format. Contrast the **long-grain press**.

short ink An ink that does not flow easily. The opposite is a **long ink**.

short sheet Sheet with too small a width dimension mixed in with sheets of the correct size.

short-term subscription Periodical subscription less than one year in duration.

short ton American ton (2000lbs) equal to .893 long (UK) tons, or .9072 metric tonnes. See **ton.**

shoulder The raised protuberance down either side of the spine of a book which is formed in the rounding and backing process. The height of the shoulder should approximate to the thickness of the board to be used for the case.

shoulder head A form of **boxed head** (q.v.) which is ranged left on a line of its own. As distinct from a **side head** (q.v.).

showcard A PoS advertising and display card, set prominently on a counter or shelf in a bookshop.

show-through The degree of **opacity** in a sheet of paper: the extent to which a printed image on one side of a page is visible from the reverse side.

shrink wrapping Enclosing in a plastic film wrapping known as **shrink wrap**.

side head A form of **boxed head** (q.v.) which is ranged left and from which the text runs on in the same line. As distinct from a **shoulder head** (q.v.).

side lay The guide on a sheet-fed press which positions the sheet sideways.

side notes Short lines of text set in the margins.

side run An addition to the **making** on a paper machine which helps to fill up the maximum width.

side-sewing Binding by sewing through the sides of the gathered sections. Also known as **McCain sewing**.

side-stabbing Used loosely to describe **side wire-stitching** (q.v.). But strictly, a form of stitching where the stitch on one side of the book penetrates only two-thirds distance, and a complementary stitch at the other side completes the securing.

sidesticks Strips of wooden furniture used when locking up a letterpress chase.

side-stitching See **side wire-stitching**.

side wire-stitching Binding by putting staples through the sections in the back margin.

signature 1. The letters of the alphabet or numerals printed at the bottom left-hand corner of sections to show the correct sequence of sections. Also, **signature mark**. 2. Synonym for **section** (q.v.).

signature mark Short statement added to the foot margin of the first page of a section giving its number in the collating sequence. Common in the days of letterpress printing, less so today.

silk screen printing Method which employs a fine mesh to support a stencil through which ink is squeezed. Also known as **screen process printing**.

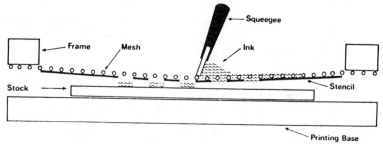

Illus 66. The elements of silk screen printing.

silurian Paper with a small percentage of long-fibred, dyed threads giving it a characteristic 'hairy' look. Used for covers or endpapers.

simplex Data communication in one direction only. Contrast **full duplex**, **half duplex**.

simultaneous transmission The transmission of data in one direction simultaneously with messages transmitted in the other. See **full duplex**.

Singer sewing Thread-sewing over a **saddle** (q.v.) through the spine of an inset book.

single-colour press Printing press capable of printing only one colour at a time.

single-colour single-sided press Basic printing press with only one unit printing one side of the paper only at each pass.

single-sheet feeder Printing machine feeding mechanism which feeds one sheet at a time to the feedboard. Slower than a **stream feeder** (q.v.).

single-sided drive A floppy disc drive that is only capable of reading or writing one side of a floppy disc. Compare **double-sided**. See also **floppy disc drive**.

sixteen-bit micro A microcomputer containing a processor that employs a sixteen-bit data word, ie which processes data in units of sixteen **bits** at a time.

size Chemical mixture used to control the water and ink absorbency of a paper. Size can be added either at the stock preparation stage (**engine-**

or **internal-sizing**); or on the paper-making machine at the **size-press** (**surface-** or **external-sizing**). Internal size can either be an alum/rosin formulation, or a mixture of synthetic resins; external size is often starch. See also **neutral sized**.

size press The unit half way down the dry end of a papermachine that applies a small quantity of surface size or of coating mix to each side of the paper web as it passes through.

size-press coated paper Paper given a very light coating (around 4gsm per side) in the **size press** unit on the paper-making machine. Also known as **pigmented paper**, **light-coated paper** or **lick-coated paper**.

sizing 1. Treatment of paper with **size** (q.v.). 2. See **scaling**.

skid A **pallet**.

skiver A book covering made of split sheep skins.

slabbing off Removing several outer layers from a reel of paper typically because they are unsatisfactory for printing through damage, dirt, marking, etc.

slave or **slave unit** A device which uses logic from a separate CPU.

slice The outlet from a paper machine's **headbox** on to the wire.

slime holes Small holes in paper resulting from a bacterial growth which developed during the making.

sling psychrometer Device for measuring relative humidity by whirling in the atmosphere.

slip case Cardboard case for book which displays the spine.

slip proof Galley proof.

slip sheeting Placing sheets of paper between printed sheets to prevent set-off.

slit Divide a web of paper along its length using a disc or wheel. As distinct from **cut**, which is to divide a web across its width using a rotating knife or guillotine blade.

slitter marks Marks on a printed sheet indicating to the binder where a slit is to be made. Used in imposition schemes which require this.

slitting the bolts Cutting open the folded edges (**bolts**) of an untrimmed section, typically in order to tip-in a single-leaf illustration.

sloped roman An imitation italic formed by electronically slanting the roman of a typeface.

slot punching Punching rectangular holes in paper.

slot scanner Fixed scanner capable of reading a **bar-code symbol** omni-directionally.

slotted binding See **notch binding**.

slug Line of metal type cast in one piece.

slur Image distortion caused by drag on the printing machine. Monitored by a **slur gauge** in most colour bars. Often caused by an excess of ink on a non-absorbent coated paper, or machine-gearing wear. See also **double**.

slushing The disintegration of fibres in a liquid.

slush pulp In papermaking, pulp in a liquid or slurry form, as opposed to dry sheets.

small capitals or **small caps** Abbreviated **sc**. Capitals the same size as the x-height of the normal lower case. As distinct from **full capitals** (q.v.)

THESE ARE SMALL CAPS. Compare with the height of normal lower case.

Illus 67. Small caps compared with lower case.

small offset Short-run litho printing using small machines (eg A4 or similar).

small pica Obsolete term for 11pt type.

SmallTalk Xerox's proprietary **operating system**, which formed the basis of the **WIMP** environment.

smashed bulk The bulk of a book-block under compression during casing-in a hard-bound book.

smashing See **nipping**.

smoothing press Rollers on a paper machine which smooth the web before drying.

smoothing roll coating Application of coating to paper surface by rollers revolving against the web direction.

smoothness Evenness of paper surface.

Smyth sewing Conventional **section-sewing** (q.v.).

snap to grids Function on graphics packages and electronic page composition systems which permits elements of a page to be positioned approximately and then automatically 'snapped' exactly into alignment to a grid by a command issued through the mouse by the operator.

SNOBOL StriNg-Oriented symBOlic Language, a programming language used in artificial intelligence applications.

snowflaking White dots on a printed piece caused by water droplets or debris.

s/o In paper descriptions, abbreviation for **substance** of, ie grammage.

soda pulp Pulp produced from hardwood chips cooked in caustic soda. See **sulphate pulp**.

soft copy Non-paper version of text, e.g. text displayed on a VDU.

soft cover Paper cover as distinct from case boards.

soft dot Half-tone dot with soft (etchable) halation around it.

soft-dot positives Film separations produced off a camera or scanner which have soft edges to the dots which can be retouched by hand.

soft format A **soft-sectored disc** format in which the length of the sector may be specified by the system designer.

soft fount In laser printing, an external software fount which is supplied on floppy disc to be downloaded into the printer's memory for output. Compare **internal fount, hard fount**.

soft hyphen A hyphen introduced into a word by an H&J program, as opposed to a **hard hyphen** grammatically essential to the word.

soft proof A representation on screen of what will be printed rather than a proof on paper or in any hard-copy form. Also, **digital proof**.

soft-sectored Describing floppy discs with a single index hole in the disc surface for synchronisation purposes, the start of sectors being identified by signals stored on the disc. Most modern computer discs are soft-sectored. Compare **hard-sectored**.

soft typesetter A desktop publishing VDU, such as a **preview screen**, usually non-interactive, showing an exact replica of a piece of work as it will appear in print. See **wysiwyg**.

software Computer programs.

software package A set of programs written for a specific purpose, e.g.

word processing.

software protection Technical and/or legal method adopted to prevent unauthorised usage.

softwood kraft See **bleached softwood kraft.**

softwood pulp Pulp made from softwood (coniferous) trees, e.g. fir, pine, spruce. As distinct from **hardwood pulp** (q.v.).

solid 1. Typeset with no leading between the lines. 2. Printed area with 100 per cent ink coverage.

solid density patches Patches of solid for each of the process inks in a colour bar testing strip. They reveal print density for each of the four colours across the sheet.

solid setting Typeset lines with no extra **leading** (q.v.).

> These are lines of type set solid
> These are lines of type set solid
> These are lines of type set solid
> These are lines of type set solid
> These are lines of type set solid

Illus 68. Solid setting.

solid state Electronic components which use solid materials for current manipulation, e.g. transistors.

solvent Ink dissolver.

sort 1. A single character of type. 2. To order data into a given sequence, e.g. alphabetical.

sort key Part of a data record used to determine the position into which the whole record will be sorted. See **sort.**

source code or **source language** The programming language in which a user's program is written, usually a **high-level language** (q.v.).

source program Program written in a language which requires subsequent translating into an **object program** which the computer can understand. Typically, a source program will be written in a **high-level language** and translated by a **compiler** into an object program in **machine-code.** Alternatively the source program may be written in a **low-level language** and translated by an assembler into an object program in machine-code.

space An impulse (or lack of impulse) which indicates a binary zero.

space An impulse (or lack of impulse) which indicates a binary zero. Compare **mark**.

spacebands Spacing pieces used by linecasting machines.

spaces Pieces of metal type used to space out letters or words.

spanner In text setting, a heading which goes across — spans — two or more columns of text.

S paper See **stabilization paper**.

spatial resolution In scanning or output technology, resolution in terms of the physical distance between samples (dots, spots, pixels per inch) as distinct from resolution in terms of the degree of tone present in a sample. The latter is called **tonal resolution** (q.v.).

spec Specification.

special colour A printing ink colour mixed specially for a job rather than made up out of the process colour set. Means an extra printing **working**.

special furnish Term to describe papers made from a mixture of woodfree and mechanical pulps, and particularly those containing improved mechanical pulps such as **CTMP** and **BCTMP** which fall somewhere in between traditional woodfree pulp and traditional mechanical pulp definitions.

speciality papers Papers for special industrial or commercial use, often with unusual properties.

special sort Unusual character necessary in a job.

specimen Sample page set to show the typography.

speckle See **skips**.

spectro-photometer Instrument that measures paper colour from its reflected light.

spectrum Complete range of colours from long wavelengths (red) to short wavelengths (blue).

speech recognition Pertaining to systems that recognise key spoken words as commands. These may be interpreted from waveform or vocal chord vibration patterns. Compare **speech synthesis**.

speech synthesis Pertaining to systems that produce sounds that correspond to spoken words. Compare **speech recognition**.

spelling check program or **spellchecker** or **spelling checker** A computer program which checks the accuracy of each word of input against the spellings of a dictionary held in memory and displays discrepancies on the VDU screen.

spiking Inconstant surges in power on an electrical power line causing interference with sensitive electronic equipment.

spine The binding edge of a book.

spine brass See **brass**.

spine lettering The words on a spine of a book, often blocked in gold or silver.

spine preparation The steps involved in preparing the spine of a book during hardback cased binding.

spinner Revolving stand for displaying books.

spiral binding Binding using a continuous spiral of wire or plastic threaded through punched holes in the back margin. Also called **mechanical binding**.

spirit duplication Duplication by moistening a carbon dye on a master to transfer it to sheets.

splice Crosswise joint in a web of paper, secured with adhesive. See also **flying paster**.

split boards Cover boards in two layers between which are glued the edges of the endpapers and section tapes in hand-bound books.

split fountain or **split duct working** Colour printing technique which divides the ink duct to achieve different colours across different parts of the same roller.

split run Print run of a publication divided in two (or more) stages to accommodate changes in text, changes of binding style etc.

split screen The displaying of more than one image at the same time on the screen of a VDU. See also **windows**.

splitting Tearing of paper suface areas on the press.

spoilage Waste incurred during the printing or binding processes.

spooling Refers to the simultaneous printing of a text whilst the user is engaged on some other activity, such as editing another text. The term comes from the acronym SPOOL, standing for Simultaneous Peripheral Output On Line.

spot Painting out unwanted light-spots on a negative with a purple water-soluble ink called **opaque**.

spot colour Single additional second colour printed in a black working.

spotted negatives Negatives which have been painted to delete any unwanted light-spots.

spot varnish Varnish applied to selected parts of a printed sheet. Often used to enhance the sheen of photographs.

spray Chemical used to spray printed sheets to prevent set-off. Also, **anti set-off spray**.

spraying Ejection of ink off the rollers, usually because it is too thin.

spread Pair of facing pages.

spread coating Method of paper coating using a controlled flow of coating material on to the paper surface.

spreading Ink creep on printed areas.

spreadsheet A software package designed to perform financial calculations. Users are presented with a grid of alphabetically-identified columns and numbered rows. Each intersection forms a cell which may contain text, numerics or algebraic formulae. As the contents of one numeric cell are altered, the contents of referenced formulae cells are updated automatically.

spring back A rounded springy back for stationery books made of stawboard or millboard.

sprinkled edges Edges of a book block sprinkled with blobs of ink.

sprocket holes Feed holes in paper tape.

square back Flat back binding.

square brackets The symbols [].

squared-up half-tone A photograph with right-angle corners, rectangular or square.

squares The parts of a case which overlap the edges of the leaves on a case-bound book.

square serif Typeface with serifs heavier than the strokes.

SRW Abbreviation for **small roundwood,** the category of log required for pulp and papermaking.

S/S 1. Abbreviation for 'same size' in reproduction specifications. 2. Abbreviation for 'single-sided' in the case of floppy discs.

stabbing See **side-stabbing** and **side wire-stitching**.

stabilisation paper or **S paper** Photographic paper used for photosetting output. Has short image-retention span once processed and cannot be used when subsequent corrections will be stripped in at a later stage. Contrast **RC paper**.

stab stitching The same as **side stitching**.

stack 1. The calendering unit on a paper machine. 2. Pile of sheets, printed or unprinted.

stack down To lay work down on to pallets.

staging Method of correcting photo-engravings by **stopping out** (q.v.) and re-etching.

stamping See **blocking**.

stamping die Steel or brass plate used for blocking. See **brass**.

stamping foil See **foil**.

stand-alone A self-contained hardware system which needs no other machine assistance to function.

standard artwork Artwork drawn for common use and made available in printed form for further reproduction. Often sold as books or as a subscription service. See also **clip art**.

standard document A word processing file containing a document that can be merged with variable information to produce a letter. See **mail merge**.

standard testing conditions Officially specifed conditions under which paper is tested: 50% relative humidity and 23⁰C.

standing film Film stored after printing or proofing pending subsequent re-use.

standoff The white space around an illustration that separates it from text that is running round it (US).

starch paste Adhesive paste formulated from starch products. In book binding, often used like **PVA** adhesive for endpaper pasting or for casing in.

star network One in which each device is connected to a central controller. As terminal to terminal communication is not possible, the entire network will become inoperable if the central computer fails. Compare **ring network**.

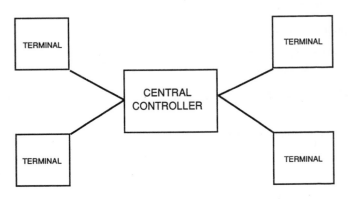

Illus 69. The principle of a star network.

starred roll Paper roll with buckled inner layers caused by loose winding and forming a 'star' pattern when viewed from end-on.

start of text A data communications control character that terminates a message heading indicating that the text of the message follows.

startup disc See **system disc**.

star wheels Toothed transport wheels on a printing machine which carry the printed sheets through to the delivery mechanism.

state of the art Pertaining to what can be achieved without further research or development.

static neutraliser An attachment on a litho press which removes static electricity from the paper.

station Unit of a binding or wrapping machine.

stationery binding Binding which allows books to remain flat when open (to facilitate writing in).

steel engraving Intaglio plate often used to reproduce fine designs on stationery (e.g. bank notes, share certificates, etc.).

stem Upright stroke of a letter or figure.

step-and-repeat machine A device which exposes the same image repeatedly according to pre-programmed instructions.

step index Index letters in the far edge margins of a book revealed by cutting the margins away progressively to expose the letters sequentially positioned from top to bottom throughout the text. Also known as **cut-through index**.

stepping See **indexing**.

stereotype Duplicate printing plate cast in a mould taken from the original. Abbreviated to **stereo**.

stet Proofreader's instruction meaning ignore the correction marked, ie, let it stand as it was.

stick See **composing stick**.

sticker Publicity material gummed for sticking on other literature or display surfaces.

stick fount Typewriter or other **non-wysiwyg** style of fount, as displayed on a VDU screen.

stickies Awkward viscous impurities in deinked and recovered pulp.

stiffness Rigidity of a sheet of paper.

stillage Pallet.

stipple Dots used to give a background effect of colour tint.

stitch To stitch with thread or staple with wire as a binding function.

STM Scientific, technical and medical publishing.

stock 1. Liquid pulp prior to papermaking. 2. (Loosely) the chosen paper to be printed.

stone The surface (now metal) on which pages of metal type are assembled and planed down (levelled). Hence, **stoneman**.

stone groundwood mechanical pulp SGW Basic mechanical pulp, obtained by grinding debarked logs against a milling stone under heat and pressure. See also **refiner mechanical pulp (RMP)**, **thermomechanical pulp (TMP)**, **chemi-thermomechanical pulp (CTMP)**.

stone out To remove small areas of a litho plate with an abrasive stone.

stop The ending of a rule where it crosses another line.

stop bit A communications code used in **asynchronous transmission** which indicates the end of a character.

stop code A word processing control code, inserted within the body of a document, designed to stop printed output for the insertion of variable information.

stopping out Protecting selected half-tone areas during etching so that they are not further reduced.

storage Floppy disc, hard disc, or magnetic tape used to store digital information in a permanent form.

storyboard Illustrated board showing proposed camera shots with script and technical annotation.

straddle heads Headings which go across the centre of a column of text. Also, **cross-heads**.

straight matter Straightforward text setting.

straight printing Printing one side of a sheet at a time, as distinct from **perfecting** (q.v.).

strawboard Originally, board made from straw fibres. Now used loosely to mean **caseboard** of any description.

stream feeder Fast feeder on a printing machine or folder which overlaps sheets as it arranges them for the grippers. Contrast **single-sheet feeder, friction feeder**.

stress Angle of shading (thickening of the main strokes) in typeface character design. May be oblique (ie, inclined at 45 degrees downwards) or vertical (ie, perpendicular). Character designs with no particular stress are known as **monoline.**

stretch wrapping Heavy-duty cling-film wrapping, used for pallets of paper, reels, and for pallets of books.

striations Jagged step-like outlines to letters or images (also called '**jaggies**') seen at their worst when low-resolution output devices attempt to output 45-degree lines. Striations occur when the resolving power of an output device is insufficient to allow a smooth outline to be formed. Striations can tend to occur with any large sizes of type output from third or fourth generation imagesetters. See also **indexing**.

strike See **stop**.

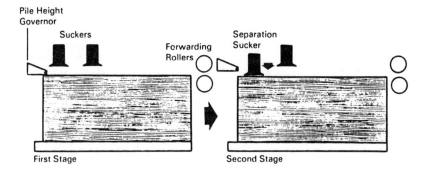

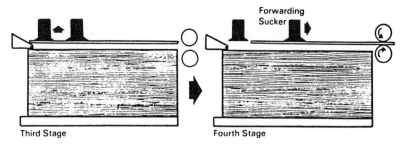

Illus 70. The principle of stream feeding.

strike-on composition Typewriter-type setting, e.g. IBM Composer. See also **golfball typewriter**.

strike-through Too heavy a printing impression which leads to the printed image bleeding through to the underside of the sheet.

string A sequence of alphabetic or numeric codes in a computer program or in phototypesetting.

string variable Programming variables that may contain alphanumeric data.

strip and rebind Remove the case of a casebound book and rebind as a paperback with a limp cover.

strip gumming Applying water-soluble adhesive to paper strips.

strip in To insert or assemble one piece of film with others, using tape or adhesive.

stripper film Very thin film used for hand corrections.

stripping Film handling, correction and assembly.

stripping guide Layout for film assembly.

stripping-in Inserting or assembling film in pieces using tape or adhesive.

strip test Use of special paper to test the **pH** (q.v.) of an offset fountain solution.

structured programming A method of program design and structure intended to aid the **debugging** process.

stub The first part of a hyphenated word at the end of a line. Some typesetting systems permit the definition of a 'minimum stub' at the end of turned-over lines.

studio system or **studio front-end system** Typesetting front-end system similar to DTP in its concept with **wysiwyg** correcting facilities, a **wimp** operating environment, and **text-and-tone** output capabilities.

stuffer Publicity material sent out in the mail with other literature.

stump The same as **stub** (q.v.).

stump line or **stub line** The last line of a page ending with a hyphen. Considered very undesirable.

style Used in a number of DTP programs to signify type face (type style).

style of the house Typographic and linguistic rules of a publishing house. Also **house style**.

style sheets Word processing or typesetting front-end program files that specify the design of printed or typeset output by requiring the operator to complete a menu of options.

sub 1.Sub editor, journalist who edits copy. 2. Subscription to a magazine or journal.

sub heading Secondary level of heading on a printed piece.

sub master Diazo film copy used for plate-making.

sub routine Set of instructions in a computer program which perform a constantly-repeated operation such as a mathematical function.

subscript Inferior character. Small character printed below the base line as part of mathematic equation. Also, **inferior**.

subscriptions Orders for a book.

subsidiary rights All the rights which subsist in a published work: the right to translate the work and issue it in a foreign language; the right to produce a case-bound book as a paperback version; the right to serialise the work; the right to make a film based on the work; etc. Subsidiary rights are sold by the originating publisher to his client for a negotiated fee, which either might be an outright payment, or be a royalty on sales.

subsidiary text Extracts, footnotes, as other secondary text in a book. Typically set smaller than the **body text**.

substance Paper weight measured in grams per square metre.

substrate 1. Base paper before coating. 2. Carrier for another material or coating, e.g. film. 3. Surface being printed on.

subtractive primaries Yellow, magenta and cyan, the process colours. Each is the result of subtracting one of the three **additive primaries** from the spectrum, leaving the other two-thirds.

suction feeder Any machine feeder which uses air blowers and suckers to separate and lift sheets.

sulphate pulp Also known as **kraft pulp**. Pulp made from wood fibres cooked in an alkaline mixture containing caustic soda (sodium hydroxide), sodium sulphide and sodium sulphate. Particularly suited to hardwoods, but increasingly used for softwoods too.

sulphite pulp Pulp made from wood fibres cooked in an acidic mixture containing calcium bisulphite and sulphur dioxide in water. Particularly suited to softwoods.

supercalendering The use of a calendering **stack** with alternate hard steel rollers and soft rollers which imparts a high gloss finish to paper as it 'slips' between them. Supercalendering is done off-machine. See illustration overleaf.

supercalendered mechanical See **WSOP**.

supercomputer A very powerful mainframe computer used where extremely high speeds and storage are required.

superior See **superscript**.

supermicro Micro capable of supporting other terminals in a network, with much the same capabilities as a minicomputer.

superscript Small figure printed above the mean line of a piece of text as a reference mark or as part of a mathematical equation. Often referred to as a superior.

These[1] figures[2] are[3] superiors[4] or[5] superscript[6].

Illus 71. Superscript or superior characters.

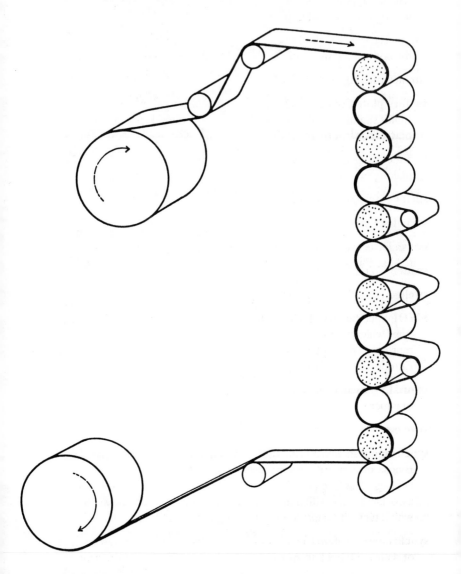

Illus 72. A supercalender.

supplement Additional part of a publication, giving extra (often late) information.

support In computing software terminology, 'supporting' a function means providing the facility to run that function. For example, a printer which 'supports' PostScript is one that is provided with the programs to accept and run PostScript code.

supported sleeve Cylindrical, wire-mesh sleeve which can be fitted over the body of a **dandy roll** and removed when not required.

surface picking See **picking**.

surface plate Conventional presensitised litho plate in which the image stands slightly proud of the surface. Compare **deep-etch plate, bimetal plate, trimetal plate**.

surface sizing Sizing of paper carried out on the sizing press of the paper-making machine.

surface strength Resistance of paper surface to picking or lifting.

surprint Exposure of a second image on an already exposed image.

swash letter An ornamental character, usually an italic cap.

swatch Colour specimen printed on paper or a set of such specimens.

swelled rules Rules which are wider at the centre than at the ends.

SWOP Specifications for Web Offset Publications: a set of recommendations widely followed in the US for the preparation and presentation of repro material to the printer. Similar to the FIPP Specifications for European Offset Printing current in Europe.

sword hygroscope Probe used to determine the moisture content of a stack of paper.

sync bit A bit used for data communicationssynchronisation.

synchronous In data transmission, signals co-ordinated by timing pulses. Blocks of data are transmitted at a measured rate dictated by timing devices at both ends of the interface. Synchronous transmission is associated more with mini or mainframe computers than with micros, which typically transmit in **asynchronous** mode (q.v.).

synchronous modem One with an internal clock which produces streams of data at a fixed transmission rate. See synchronous transmission.

synchronous transmission Data transmission in which each bit is transmitted at a given rate. Synchronous transmission is capable of higher speeds than **asynchronous transmission** but requires that both transmitter and receiver remain in exact synchronisation.

syntax The rules of grammar regulating the use of a language.

synthetic papers Synthetic materials, typically plastic, which have many of the properties of paper and can be printed. Usually expensive.

synthetic resins See under **resins**.

system disc In computing, a disc which carries on it the basic operating-system files which enable it to load of its own accord when the computer is first switched on. Also, **boot-up disc, startup disc**.

system functions Functions relating to the movement of data within a system and controlled from the keyboard, e.g. writing to memory, or transmission between peripherals.

system generation An operating system utility that allows a user to customise an operating system and related **applications programs** to suit hardware requirements.

System Network Architecture IBM's distributed data processing network architecture.

T

tab index Index letters printed on tabs which are stuck to the far edge margin of a book.

table Data stored in a form, often an array, that is suitable for reference.

tabloid Newspaper size half the size of a **broadside** sheet and approximating to A3.

tabular material Typeset tables or columns of figures.

tack The viscosity and stickiness of ink.

tacketing Method of strengthening stationery binding using 'slips' or bands of leather.

tackmeter An instrument designed to measure ink tack properties.

tag A generic mark-up tag is one which identifies a particular attribute: an 'A' heading, for example, in the mark-up of text. Tags are converted to typesetting by allocating typographical specifications to them and translating them inside the front-end of the typesetting system. Tags placed in a text electronically (as in **ASPIC**) can be directly converted by using a **search and replace** routine in the output computer.

tailband Cotton or silk cord attached to the foot of the spine of a book. See also **headband**.

tail-end hook See **back-edge curl**.

tail-piece Typographical device at the end of a chapter or book.

*Illus 73. A tail-piece from an early edition of **Aesop's Fables**.*

tails Bottom margins of pages.

take An amount of copy for typesetting allocated to one operator. Part of a newspaper story which has been divided up for speed of setting.

tall Upright, or **portrait** in format.

tandem press Another term for a **common-impression press** (q.v.).

tandem working Using more than one printing machine in-line.

tape See **punched tape**.

tape editing Correcting information stored on tape, usually resulting in a second, edited tape.

tape merging The combining of data from a master tape and a correction tape to produce a third error-free tape.

tape streamer A magnetic tape transport designed to perform back-up operations.

tape transport The device which moves tape past the reading heads.

taping Pasting strips of material to binding sections to add strength.

TAPPI See **Technical Association of the Pulp and Paper Industry**.

tare Weight of an empty container or unloaded vehicle.

taster Small sample of a book, typically a chapter, sent out by a publisher for promotion purposes.

TD See **transmitted data**.

tear-off menu An alternative term for a **pop-up menu** or **pull-down menu** (q.v.).

tearsheet Page from printed periodical used as proof or evidence of publication, especially of advertisement.

tear test 1. Test which determines **grain direction** in paper by the ease of tearing. 2. Test to determine strength.

Technical Association of the Pulp and Paper Industry (TAPPI) American professional organisation for pulp and papermakers.

technical press Periodicals concerned with technical subjects and circulating among specialists in those subjects.

Telecom Gold A nationwide **electronic mail** service operated by British Telecom.

telecommunications Communication over the telephone wire.

telecommuting The use of computers and telcommunications to enable a user to work away from the office.

teleordering In the UK, system for ordering books whereby a subscribing bookshop can order its books via one central computer: every 24 hours the orders are split, consolidated and distributed to the relevant publishers for fulfilment.

teleprinter Device like a typewriter attached to a telephone line originally enabling messages typed in at one end to be simultaneously reproduced on a machine at the other end. **Teletex** and **telex** are developments from the teleprinter principle.

telescoped roll Reel of paper with progressively misaligned edge.

teletex In data communications, an international business correspondence service using word processors linked by telephone lines.

teletypesetter Linecasting system driven by six-channel paper tape generated on separate keyboards.

telex An international dial-up teleprinter switching service. Each telex installation has its own code. Messages sent from one telex station to another are automatically printed out at the destination end.

template An underlying page design or **grid** into which text and graphics are placed.

template matching systems In OCR, recognition systems which work by comparing characters scanned with a table of specific templates (character shapes) held in computer memory. Template matching systems are less powerful than **pattern matching systems** (q.v.) which go down to graphics primitives level in identifying characters.

terminal Keyboard and/or screen for computer communication or text generation.

terminator See **Ethernet**.

terms The discount and other selling arrangements agreed between a bookshop and a supplying publisher.

text The body typesetting in a book as distinct from headings and display type.

text area Area occupied by text on a page, normally governed by a grid.

text editing Any rearrangement or change performed upon textual material, such as correcting, adding and deleting.

text editor In computing, an alternative term for a dedicated word-processing program or utility.

text pages The principal matter in a book as distinct from the **frontmatter** and **endmatter** (q.v.).

text paper 1. Fine quality paper for printed publicity work. 2. The body paper of a magazine or book as distinct from the cover stock.

text processing The computer editing and production of text.

text type Body type of the main text in a book. Loosely, a **composition size** of type of 14pt or less, as opposed to a **display** type.

textured screen Halftone screen that yields a textured pattern on the halftone created.

thermal printer A **non-impact printer:** heat is applied to a ribbon carrying waxed ink which is transferred to the paper in the form of dots.

thermographic printing Relief effect created by heating special powder or ink on a sheet to give 'raised' typesetting.

thermomechanical pulp Abbreviated to **TMP.** Superior, stronger **mechanical pulp** (q.v.) produced from steam-heated wood chips.

thermoplastic Describing a plastic, rubber or synthetic material which becomes and remains soft and mouldable when subjected to heat.

thermosetting Describing a plastic, rubber or synthetic which becomes permanently hard and unmouldable once subjected to heat.

thesaurus A feature of some word-processing packages. Synonyms for words can by accessed on-line by highlighting a word and activating the dictionary program behind it.

thickening image In litho printing, the progressive thickening and coarsening of an image during a press run. Its opposite is a **sharpening image**.

thick space Word space equal to one third of an em of set.

thimble A printing element similar to a daisywheel but formed into a thimble-like shape.

thinners Solvents added to ink to reduce tack.

thin space Word space equal to one-fifth of an em of set.

third-generation computers Computers in which **integrated circuits** − silicon chips − first replaced transistors.

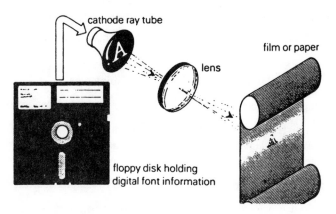

Illus 74. The imaging system of a third-generation photosetter.

third-generation photosetters Photosetters using cathode ray tubes to generate the typographical images.

thirty The symbol **-30-** is used on some newspapers to indicate the end of a story in copy.

thirty-two bit micro A microcomputer containing a microprocessor chip which deals with data in blocks of 32 binary **bits** at a time (32-bit computer 'words').

thixotropy A property of some gels and emulsions, and typical of litho ink, that they become fluid when agitated, but when left still, turn thick. Thixotropy is a major cause of an ink 'hanging back' in the ink duct on press rather than flowing forward unless it is properly agitated.

threadless binding See **adhesive binding**.

thread-sealing Binding method using meltable threads as 'staples' to secure individual sections through their backs before they are trimmed and forwarded on for gathering.

thread sewing Conventional sewing. Also known as **French sewing** or **section sewing**.

thread stitching Securing inset books by stitching through the spine with threads.

three-colour process Process work using the yellow, magenta and cyan without black.

three-five-seven rule The crudest form of hyphenation logic which permits words to be broken after the third, fifth or seventh letter. Inadequate for all but the most undemanding purposes. See under **hyphenation logic**.

three-point register A technique for obtaining register by taking two adjacent sides of a rectangle and aligning them to three points - two along the top long edge, and one down the short edge.

three-quarter binding Method in which the majority of the case of a book is covered in leather or cloth and the remainder is finished in a different material.

throwaway Free newspaper comprised largely of advertisements.

throw-out A page which folds out of a book or magazine to a size larger than the book trim. Also **fold-out, gatefold**.

thumb index Index where the alphabetical divisions are cut into the edge of the book trim.

thumbnail sketch Small rough drawing.

ticket board Pasteboard.

tick marks Alternative term for **crop marks** or **cut marks** (q.v.).

tied letters See **ligature**.

TIFF Tagged Image File Format. A standard file format in both the AppleMac and IBM PC environments for the storage and transmission of all scanned images, and typically high-resolution bitmaps such as photographs. Scanned images are freely accepted into a number of page composition software packages if they are first converted into TIFF files.

tight Laid out on a page so that there is little white space.

tightback binding Binding in which the backs of the sections are stuck to the spine of the book, reinforcing its strengh. Also known as **fastback binding**.

tight edges Referring to a stack of paper in which the edges of the sheets are stretched tight and the centre of the sheets are baggy. Caused by the stack having a higher moisture level than the surrounding atmosphere. Compare **wavy edges**.

time-sharing Concurrent processing of several jobs or programs on a computer.

tint A solid colour reduced in shade by screening. Specified as a percentage of the solid colour, and in a particular **screen ruling** (q.v.).

tint generator Program on an **epc system** which generates tints inside a designated area.

tinting In litho printing, an unwanted light coloured tint which prints all over the non-image area of the sheet. It is caused by ink entering and contaminating the fountain solution. Not to be confused with **scumming** (q.v.).

tint laying Using films to create a **tint** (q.v.).

tip in 1. To fix a single leaf inside a section. 2. A single leaf placed in this way. Tipping in is invariably a manual process.

tip on To fix a single leaf, or endpaper, to the outside of a section. Tipping on can sometimes be mechanised using an endpapering machine.

tissue A fine, thin paper used for a variety of purposes where a delicate, lightweight paper is required.

titanium dioxide Mineral used in paper-making to add brightness and opacity.

title page Page of a book carrying the title, author's name and publisher's name. Always a recto.

titling Type fount only available in full-faced caps.

TMP Thermomechanical pulp (q.v.).

toggle Any electronic device having two states. In word processing, any command which, in identical form, is used to both switch a function on and off (underlining, for example).

tombstone Basic advertisement for professional services which conforms to the limitations imposed by law or by professional associations.

ton In ascending order of magnitude there come the US ton (**short ton**) of 2000lbs, the metric **tonne** of 1000Kgs (2204lbs), and the UK ton (**long ton**) of 2240lbs. In metric terms, the first comes to 907Kgs, the second to 1000Kgs, and the third to 1016Kgs.

tonal resolution The number of **grey scales** (q.v.) which can be detected by a device. Sometimes called **grey scale determination**.

tone Continuous tone, with intermediate shades of grey between black and white, as distinct from **line** which is either solid black or pure white. Tone subjects must be reproduced by the **halftone** method.

toner Chemical used to create the image in photocopying processes.

tonne Metric tonne of 1000Kgs, just under 2% smaller than the imperial (UK) **ton,** and just over 10% larger than the US **short ton.** The exact equivalents are .984 long (UK) tons, or 1.102 short (US) tons.

tooth Rough surface, as applied to a paper.

toothy Having a rough surface.

top of form A character printer feature that advances paper by one page.

top side The side of a web facing upwards during making, i.e. opposite to the **wire side.** Also called the **felt-side** and the **right-side.** Tends to be smoother than the wire-side.

top wire In papermaking, the upper wire of a duoformer paper machine.

torn-tape system Paper tape typesetting system involving manual removal and feeding of tape from one machine to another.

to view Referring to the number of pages appearing on one side of a plate or sheet, e.g. 32-to-view = 32pp each side of the sheet = 64pp unit.

tpi See **tracks per inch.**

tpy In papermaking, **tonnes per year,** the common criterion on which a papermill's output is measured. A typical book paper mill might produce somewhere between 50-75tpy of uncoated book grades off one or two machines. Larger-scale newsprint or **LWC** mills might produce anywhere upwards from 200tpy off one or two machines.

tracing paper Transparent paper manufactured for tracing.

track 1. In printing, the line or strip around the circumference of the printing plate governed by one inking key. All items positioned in this track will be subject to the same density of inking on the press run. Also called **zone.** 2. In computing, one of the concentric rings of a disc, subdivided into **sectors,** along which data is stored. In a disc pack, a collection of tracks in the same relative position under each other is known as a **cylinder** (q.v.).

tracker ball An alternative to a mouse or to cursor keys as a pointing device. The ball is mounted in a enclosure lined with sensors which detect the direction and speed of rotation. See **mouse, puck.**

tracking 1. When illustrations are in **track** (q.v.) on the press, they are subject to the same density of ink. The 'tracking' of subjects means their positions relative to each other along the same track. 2. See **track kerning**.

track kerning Global reduction in letterspacing to achieve a tighter visual effect. The same as **character compensation** (q.v.).

tracks per inch A measure of the density of tracks on a hard or floppy disc: the number of concentric rings (tracks) which are contained in one inch of radius. A common track density for 3.5" micro floppies, for example, is 135tpi.

tractor feed A printer drive mechanism comprising a chain or belt equipped with teeth which engage with the sprocket holes of continuous stationery.

trade discount Discount allowed by a publisher to wholesaler or retail bookshop.

trade houses Companies in the printing industry whose main work is for other printers. Often specialists in a specific operation, e.g. laminating.

trademark Unique printing mark identifying a company.

trade press Periodicals targeted to specific trades or businesses.

trade publishing The publishing of general-interest books which are sold through the retail bookshop trade.

trade tolerance Allowance for under or over delivery quantities deemed acceptable commercially. Applies particularly to paper, with reference to the Paper Trade Customs.

trade typesetting A **trade typesetter** is one whose livelihood is typesetting. As distinct from in-house typesetting, or typesetting as a facility offered as part of a total print-bind service.

transceiver See **Ethernet**.

transducer Electronic device which converts input signals of one type into output of a different nature.

transfer type Pressure-sensitive type on carrier sheets. Can be rubbed off to create type in position on the page. Also known as **transfer lettering**.

transistor A component made up of layers of different semiconducting materials which, when a current is fed to one of its three terminals, controls the flow of current between the other two conductors.

Transitional Category of type style exemplified by Baskerville and marking the transition from **Old Style** designs to **Modern** designs.

abcdefghijklmnopqrstuvwxyz
ABCDEFGHIJKLMNOPQRSTUVW
XYZ 1234567890 1234567890 .,;:'‘«»&!?

Illus 75. Baskerville, a Transitional typeface.

translation table See **look up table**.

translator Portmanteau term for any **compiler, interpreter** or **assembler** conversion program that translates a **high-level language** or **low-level language** (source code) into **machine-code** (object code).

transliterate Transcribe into characters of a different language.

transmission In computing, see **data transmission**.

transmission codes Standard codes or **code sets** used in computers to represent alphanumeric characters and numbers. Examples include **ASCII, EBCDIC,** and **TTS** (q.v.).

transmission copy Copy which is viewed by transmitted light, e.g. a transparency. As distinct from **reflection copy** (q.v.) which is viewed by reflected light.

transparency Full-colour photographic positive on transparent film for viewing by transmitted light. Suitable as copy for separation.

transparency viewer Box arrangement with special light source to enable the viewing of transparencies under consistent conditions.

transparent In computing, a process is **transparent to the user** if he is unaware of it going on. Used particularly of computer processing which is taking place as an operator is doing something else.

transparent copy Transparencies (q.v.).

transparent inks Inks such as process Inks which permit other colours to show through when overprinted and so produce subsequent mixed colours.

transpose Abbreviated **trs.** Exchange the position of words, letters or lines, especially on a proof. Hence **transposition**.

transputer Computer consisting of a single chip.

trap Superimposition of one colour on another when printing. Trapping characteristics are often monitored by a test strip in the **colour bars** printed on a four-colour job.

trichromatic Using three process colours (magenta, yellow, cyan) to print in full colour.

trim Cut edges off sheets to square up or reduce size. Hence **trimmed size** is the size after trimming.

trimask Special photographic mask made of three-layer film and used in camera separation processes to colour correct separations as they are made.

trimetal plate Lithographic plate for very long-run work where three layers of metal are used in manufacturing the plate.

trim marks Alternative term for **crop marks** (q.v.) or **tick marks**.

trimmed size or **trimmed page size** In printing and binding, the finished size of the job in its completed form. Contrast **untrimmed size**.

trim to bleed Trim so that printed solids reach the edge of the trimmed sheet.

triplex board Board made up of three layers of thinner paper or of one central layer lined on both sides with paper.

TROFF Abbreviation for **Typesetter runoff format:** a file format associated with typesetting programs running under the UNIX operating system.

troubleshoot To find and rectify a fault in hardware or software.

true dictionary See **dictionary**.

true italics Italic fount designed as such, as distinct from an electronically contrived **sloped roman**.

true small caps Small caps designed as such, rather than created as a smaller size of main-text capitals (in which case the strokes frequently look too thin).

truncation In bar-code design, a symbol which is printed to normal width but with reduced height. Truncated symbols cannot always be read omni-directionally.

TS Abbreviation for typescript.

TTS Six-level code set used by teletypesetters and taken over into some phototypesetting (Linotype) applications.

tty See teletype.

turned 1. A table or illustration turned sideways on a page so as to fit better. Whether on a verso or recto page, turned tables or illustrations should always be rotated so that the foot of them is on the right-hand side of the page when the book is in normal, upright, position. 2. News setting carried over on to another page.

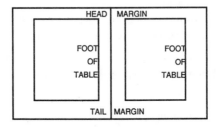

Illus 76. The correct positioning for turned illustrations or tables.

turned in Cover material turned over the edges of the board.

turner bar Bar on a web offset press which redirects the web through a right-angle degree.

turnkey system A system which is complete and designed for a specific use. With hardware this implies that the supplier has full responsibility for installation, with software the implication is that the user may initiate the package without necessarily understanding or even being aware of the operating system.

twice-up Instruction to prepare artwork at 200% of finished size.

twin-wire Smooth board or paper made from two separate webs which are brought together at the press section of the **twin-wire paper machine**. Contrast the **duoformer** principle (q.v.) with which it is sometimes confused.

two-colour press Two-unit machine which can print two colours on a sheet in a single pass.

two-letter index Index based on divisions of two letters in each section.

two-revolution press Letterpress machine where the impression cylinder revolves twice for each sheet: once to make the impression and then to rise clear of the type for delivery of the sheet.

two's complement A method of representing a negative value in binary arithmetic, the negative being obtained by complementing the digits and adding one to the result.

two-set Printing two sets of the same image or of the same lot of pages on the same sheet. After printing each sheet yields two copies. Also, **four-set**, **six-set**, etc.

two-sheet detector A device for stopping a printing press or other sheet-fed machine when more than one sheet is fed.

two-shot binding Adhesive binding in which the first application is of **PVA** adhesive, the second of **hot-melt** adhesive. Compare **one-shot** binding.

two-sidedness Undesirable differing finish between the **felt-side** and the **wire-side** of a sheet.

two up Printing or binding two sets together to allow a better usage of a press.

tying-up Using cord to secure type for storage.

Type An operating system command used to display the contents of a text file.

type area The area occupied by text on a page.

typecasting Setting type in metal by a machine such as a Linotype or Intertype.

type depth The depth to which the type on a page falls, measured either in lines, pica ems, or mm/inches.

typeface A specifically designated style of type, e.g. Times or Helvetica.

type family Roman, italic, bold and all other versions of one typeface.

type gauge A rule calibrated in picas for measuring type.

type height In letterpress printing, the distance from the foot of the type to the printing surface: 23.317mm in the UK and USA.

type measure See **measure**.

type metal The alloy for cast type, comprising lead, tin and antimony.

type scale See **type gauge**.

typescript Typed copy. Also, **manuscript**.

type series All the sizes available in one style of typeface, eg 8pt, 9pt, 10pt, etc, of the Baskerville (roman) series.

typesetter command language The computer language which controls the operations of a typesetting machine. Also called a **typesetter driver**, or **driver** (q.v.).

typesetting The composition, assembly and laying out of text to professional typographical standards.

typewriter composition See **strike-on composition**.

typographer Designer of printed material.

typographic errors Abbreviated to **typos**. See **literals**.

typography 1. The art of designing type for printing. 2. The arrangement or general appearance of typematter.

U

u and lc, also **ulc, U/L** Abbreviation for upper and lower case. Instruction to follow copy for caps and lower case.

UART See **Universal Asynchronous Receiver Transmitter**.

UCR See **undercolour removal**.

UDF See **user defined format**.

UDK See **user defined key**.

U/L or **ulc** Upper and lower case.

ultraviolet-erasable PROM A PROM that may be erased by exposure to ultraviolet light. See **PROM**.

Ultrix Digital Equipment Corporation's proprietary version of **UNIX**.

ULWC Ultra-lightweight coated: mechanical coated paper under 50gsm. See also **LWC, MWC, HWC**.

unbacked Printed one side only.

unbundling Referring to the sale of software, training and services by a computer manufacture independent of the sale of hardware.

uncoated paper Paper with no coating and therefore not suitable for high quality illustrated work.

uncompressed In an illustration file format, describes a file which holds all the information in full form before any **data compression** techniques are applied. So, for example, **uncompressed TIFF**.

undercolour removal Abbreviated to **UCR**. Technique which reduces unwanted colour in areas of overlaps. Results in better **trapping** and lower ink cost.

undercut The amount of space left for plate packing on press cylinders.

underexposure Inadequate exposure to light causing a mostly dense image. Contrast **overexposure** (q.v.).

underlay The packing under a letterpress block which brings the height up to impression level.

underline 1. Caption (US). 2. A word processing facility to automatically underline text.

underrun Paper delivery or printing quantities which fall short of the order.

underside Bottom side of a web of paper. Also known as the **wireside** or **wrong side**. The other side is the **top side**, **felt side**, or **right side** (q.v.).

unearned advance The amount by which an author's total royalty earnings for a book fall short of the **advance** he received (q.v.).

unglazed Uncalendered, plain, paper finish.

union paper Special wrapping paper comprising two webs joined by tar coating.

unit 1. Smallest subdivision into which the em character width measurement of a fount is divided. Used as the counting basis for all character widths in a fount. The actual size of a unit varies with the manufacturer's system. 2. One set of printing cylinders with the associated damping and inking systems. A four colour press will have four units, each printing one colour. See also **unit press**.

unit press A design of multi-colour litho printing press which consists of any number of single printing units, one for each colour, which can be linked together in line. Also known as the **modular** or **in-line** press design. Compare the **common-impression** press.

unit value The number of units in a character width.

Universal Asynchronous Receiver Transmitter UART A chip, used in conjunction with asynchronous devices, that converts serial data to parallel data, or vice versa. Compare **USART**, **USRT**.

Universal Product Code See **UPC**.

Universal Synchronous Asynchronous Receiver Transmitter USART A programmable chip used for synchronous or asynchronous transfer of serial data between the CPU and an input/output device. Compare **UART**, **USART**.

Universal Synchronous Receiver Transmitter USRT A device designed to control the timing of synchronous data transfer, and serial to parallel conversion. Compare **UART**, **USART**.

UNIX A multi-user operating system associated with mini computers and supermicros which allows several operators to use the same central computing resources simultaneously (**multitasking**).

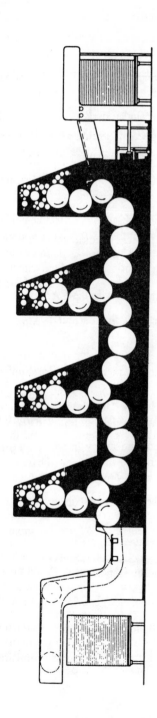

Illus 77. A typical four-unit configuration for colour printing.

unjustified Typesetting with even spacing, therefore having a ragged right edge.

unlined chipboard Caseboard made from mixed waste furnish and consisting of a number of plies of thin board pasted together. See also **Dutch grey board, millboard.**

unsewn binding See **perfect binding.**

unsharp masking USM Feature offered on most scanners enabling the edges of coloured images to be hardened where they touch each other by removing the 'fringes'.

un-shift Keyboard designation for lower case.

untrimmed size Dimensions of a sheet or printed piece before trimming.

up 1. Running (in the case of equipment). 2. Several at once: two-up means two copies the same out of one sheet.

UPC Universal Product Code: the barcode article numbering system used in the US, compatible with the **EAN** system in most major ways.

update Edit a file by adding current data.

upper case Capital letters.

upright Format in which the head to tail dimension is greater than the width dimension (ie, the normal 8vo book format). Also, **portrait.**

upward compatibility The ability of one computer to run programs written for a later model, but not vice versa.

usage alert A program utility in some word-processing and authoring packages which alerts the writer to the frequency with which he is using certain words, suggesting synonyms if required.

USART See **Universal Synchronous Asynchronous Receiver Transmitter.**

USASCII United States American Standard Code for Information Interchange, synonymous with **ASCII.** Typically, the only difference lies with the character associated with the hash in USASCII and pound symbol in ASCII.

user area That part of computer memory allocated to user programs, the remainder being reserved for buffers and operating systems.

user defined format An instruction assigned to an input key to perform a particular command or string of commands over and above any normal function. Keys programmable by the user in this way are known as **UDKs user defined keys**, or **user programmable keys**, or **macros** (q.v.)

user interface See **environment**.

USM See **unsharp masking**.

USRT See **Universal Synchronous Receiver Transmitter**.

utilities or **utility programs** Software programs designed as tools to assist in the writing and development of systems, the analysis or recovery of data, etc.

uv varnish Ultra-violet varnish. Sometimes installed in-line with a printing machine, a uv varnish unit deposits a high-gloss varnish dried by exposure to uv light.

V

V.21 300 baud **modem** standard for use with the general switched telephone network.

V.22 1200-baud **modem** standard for use with the general switched telephone network.

V.23 600/1200-baud **modem** standard for use with the general switched telephone network.

V.24 Data communications standard comparable with RS232C.

V.30 Parallel data transmission standard for use with the general switched telephone network.

vacuum frame Contact printing frame using vacuum pumps to hold copy in position.

vacuum tube See **first-generation computer**.

VALID An acronyn for VALue IDentification language, a **high-level** programming language.

validation The process of cross-checking, particularly with relation to data which is to be entered into a computer for further processing, and which must be checked as correct before this happens. See also **verification**.

value Lightness or darkness of tone.

Vancouver format A systematic format for laying out bibliographical references much used in **STM** publishing.

Van Dyke American term for a **brownline** or **brownprint**: type of dyeline proof.

variable A name given to a memory location which is used to hold the current value of variable data.

variable space Space between words used to justify a line. Contrast **fixed space** (q.v.).

varnish Thin, transparent coating applied to printed work for gloss or protection. Types of varnish include **machine varnish**, **NC varnish**, and **uv varnish**.

varnishing The application of any of several grades of varnish to a printed board or sheet for added gloss or protection.

vat boardmaking machine Boardmaking machine consisting of a number of vats (cylinder units) in line, each containing a large hollow cylinder (cylinder mould) revolving in the stock. The board is built up from a number of such plies joined together on a moving felt. Also, **cylinder mould machine**.

vat boards Boards made on a **vat boardmaking machine**.

vat papers Hand-made papers formed on a wire in a vat.

VDI See **Virtual Device Interface**.

VDU/VDT See **visual display unit/terminal**.

vector A line and its direction. Vector instructions given to a computer enable the computer to calculate and plot the outlines of graphics and type characters. A programmed instruction then fills in the outline. Contrast **bitmap**.

vector data Data held in vector (outline) form.

vehicle Liquid component of ink which serves to carry the **pigment** and bonds it to the substrate.

vellum 1. Prepared inner side of calf-skin, used in binding. 2. Imitation of this type of surface on paper.

velox print Term for **screened print** (q.v.).

Venetian Category of typeface otherwise known as **Humanist** (q.v.).

Venix Version of the **Unix** operating system developed by Venturcom.

Ver In MS-DOS, an operating system command that displays the current version of the operating system in use.

verification Data **validation** achieved by keying the information twice and then performing a character-by-character check.

Verify An operating system utility that confirms that data written to disc has been correctly recorded.

version A particular major 'edition' of software. An amendment within a version is termed a **release**.

verso Left-hand page with even number.

vertical justification Spacing a column or page of type to fit a predetermined depth. Automatic process on some typesetting systems. See also

feathering.

vertical screen Screen in which the orientation of the cross lines is at 90 degrees upright rather than at 45 degrees inclination as in the conventional **crossline** screen.

vertical scrolling The ability to move text displayed on a screen up or down a line at a time to reveal other parts of the text.

VGA Video Graphics Array High-resolution graphics adapter standard adopted for IBM **PS/2**. Offers 256 colours on colour monitors, or 64 shades of grey on monochrome monitors.

vibrator roller Roller in the inking system of a litho press which transfers ink from the **duct roller** of the system to the start of the **ink pyramid**. Also, **ductor roller**, **feed roller**. See also **inking system**.

video disc A variety of **optical disc** (q.v.) on which information is stored in analogue form as visual images rather than as digital data.

video display A text or graphics display device which may be a **cathode-ray tube**, **LED** or **gas plasma display**.

video printing system Computerised electronic system from Japan which takes a selected frame from a video tape, electronically enhances it, and produces a colour transparency or a set of four-colour separated films.

video scanner A video camera used as a scanner. The analogue video signals are enhanced and digitised before being passed over to a graphics editing unit for editing.

vignette Half-tone with background fading out.

virgin fibre Fibre used for the first time to make paper (i.e. not re-cycled).

Virtual Device Interface An ANSI graphics standard defining an interface between device-independent and device-dependent graphics code.

virtual disc See **RAM disc**.

virus Program code introduced into an operating system for malicious purposes. At a determined point, when a write command is encountered, for example, the virus will erase all files from a disc. Compare **worm**.

viscoelastic Flexible enough to return to original size after stretching.

viscosity Resistance to flow; tackiness.

Visicalc A proprietary **spreadsheet** package.

visual A layout or rough of artwork. Also, **mock-up.**

visual display unit/terminal VDU/VDT Cathode ray tube screen and keyboard for input and correction of copy to a computer or photosetter. VDU screens come in a number of sizes and resolutions. A popular format for text display is 80 characters across by 25 lines down, with a screen resolution of 640 pixels x 200 pixels (a character matrix of 8 dots by 8 dots at something like 72 dpi). Screens of A4 or A3 size are preferable for interactive page make up.

viz Abbreviation for Latin 'videlicet' meaning namely.

VLSI Very Large Scale Integration. The next generation of chip on from the **LSI** chip. The **VLSI** chip contains many more gates and offers expanded capabilities.

voice data entry See **speech recognition.**

voice input See **speech recognition.**

voice output See **speech synthesis.**

voice recognition See **speech recognition.**

voice synthesis See **speech synthesis.**

void hickey A **hickey** (q.v.) appearing as a white spot on the printed image.

volatile storage Storage media in which data is lost if the power supply is removed, such as the **RAM** in a microcomputer (q.v.). Compare **non-volatile storage, ROM.**

volume 1. Bound book. 2. Thickness of paper expressed as a volume number (e.g. vol 18) equal to the thickness in millimetres of 100 sheets of that particular paper in 100gsm.

volumetric A volumetric paper is one which is made to a guaranteed bulk. Typically an antique wove or bulky book wove.

voucher proofs Proofs of a job which are shown for confirmation or for reference only, and which do not need to be returned.

W

waffling Deformation of a sheet caused by excessive ink tack.

WAN Wide area network. A network of micros spread over a larger area than a **LAN** (q.v.), and linked typically by telecommunication.

wand Alternative term for **light pen** (q.v.).

warm colours Red and yellow shades.

warm start Also **warm boot**. In computing, restarting a computer without switching it off first. Certain routine self-checks have already been made, and so the computer reaches its opening prompt faster than from a cold start.

warp The long threads in a woven cloth which represent the machine direction. The cross threads are the **weft** or **woof**.

warping Deformation in the case boards of a bound book. Warping can be caused by a number of factors including differing ambient conditions between the place of production and the point of sale, packing books while damp, binding with opposing grain directions between the boards, the endpapers, and the case materials.

wash drawing Black and white illustration with tones created by grey or black ink or paint washes.

washing The unintended dissolving by water of pigment in ink during litho printing.

wash-up The cleaning of the printing units of a press prior to a change of ink or shut-down of the machine.

waste furnish Board or paper **furnish** consisting of waste paper – packaging, cardboard, newsprint, magazine papers, etc.

water finish High finish to paper achieved by damping the web as it passes through the calender stack.

water immersion size test Test using water immersion to establish the effectiveness of sizing in a paper as a water repellent.

waterleaf Moisture-absorbent paper such as blotting paper or filter paper.

watermark Design impressed into a paper web during manufacture by the **dandy roll** (q.v.).

water-soluble inks Used in screen printing and gravure.

water vapour transmission rate Test to determine the waterproof qualities of packaging paper.

wavy edges Referring to a stack of paper in which the edges of the sheets are baggy and the centre of the sheets are stretched tight. Caused by the stack having a higher moisture level than the surrounding atmosphere. Compare **tight edges**.

wax engraving Engraving produced by using wax as a mould for an **electro** (q.v.). Used particularly for rule work.

wax test Test of **picking** (q.v.) of paper surface using graded wax sticks.

wayzegoose Printer's annual outing or dinner.

web A continuous length of paper (i.e. a **roll** or **reel**) as distinct from sheets.

web-fed Presses printing on **webs** (q.v.) of paper rather than sheets.

web offset Reel-fed **offset litho** (q.v.). May be **heat-set** (q.v.) or **cold-set** (q.v.). A variety of possible configurations are possible ranging from one mono unit with a single reel-stand up to multi-unit colour presses with up to three reel-stands.

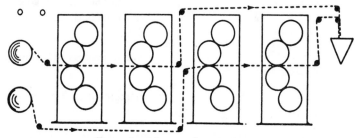

Two webs with two colours both sides

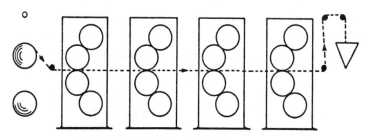

Single web with four colours both sides

Illus 78. Two typical web offset press configurations.

web press See **web-fed** (q.v.).

web sized mechanical sc paper See **WSOP**.

web sized offset printing paper See **WSOP**.

web tension Adjustable degree of lateral pull on a web of paper in a web press.

weft The cross threads in a woven material. Contrast **warp**.

weight 1. In typography, the degree of boldness of a type-face style (e.g. light, medium, etc). 2. Loosely, in paper specification, the **substance** (q.v.).

wet end That part of a Fourdrinier paper machine that comprises the wire section and the pressing section.

wet-on-dry printing Multicolour printing on a single colour press. Each successive colour is printed on top of a dry film of ink. Contrast **wet-on-wet printing.**

wet-on-wet printing The printing of one colour directly after another as on a multi-unit printing press (i.e. before each colour has dried). As distinct from four-colour printing on a single colour press, where each working has to dry before the next colour is applied, and each colour is a separate working.

wet printing See **wet-on-wet printing.**

wet proof See **machine proof.**

wet stock Pulp in its liquid form or during formation on the wire.

wet strength Tensile strength of saturated paper.

wetting agent An additive which decreases the surface tension of water.

wf Wrong fount. Proofreader's mark indicating an incorrect typefount has been used in setting.

wheel printer A printer with printable characters held on metal wheels. Compare **drum printer**.

whip stitching Sewing technique used to join sheets at the edges.

whirler Machine which applies photosensitive coating to printing plates.

whiteback Cloth which is dyed on its surface only, with the reverse side remaining white. Contrast **dyed-through** cloth.

white line Line of space in phototypesetting.

white out See **reverse out**.

white waste Plain unprinted waste paper used as a furnish for recycled paper.

whitewater See **backwater**.

whiting A widely used **extender** (q.v.) for ink.

whole-bound Full bound case of a hard-bound book covered in the same material all over. Also, **full-bound**.

wholesaler Person or firm that buys books in large quantities from a publisher and resells them to booksellers. The equivalent in the schools world is the **educational contractor** (q.v.), and in the library world the **library supplier**.

widow or **widow line** Short last line of a paragraph at the top of a page. Considered undesirable. See also **paragraph widow, orphan**.

width card Information contained on a card which programs a photosetter or laser printer for the set widths of a particular typefount.

WIMP environment A user-friendly style of interface, based on windows, icons, a mouse, and pull-down menus. This style of interface, in the shape of the Finder operating system, was first adopted by Apple for its Macintosh computer. It has since been emulated by the Microsoft Windows environment and Digital Research's GEM which run on IBM and DEC computers respectively.

Winchester disc Hard disc with extensive backing store capacity. See **hard disc**.

winder In papermaking, a slitting and re-reeling machine.

window 1. Clear panel left in litho film for half-tones to be stripped in. 2. Portion of a VDU screen dedicated to a particular file/document. Several windows can be open on-screen at one time, allowing the user to jump from one to another rapidly. Ideal operating conditions for on-screen cut and paste.

Windows Standard graphical user interface for IBM micros, written by Microsoft. Provides the same kind of user interface as on the Apple Macintosh.

wing effect The result of out-of-square guillotining of a book: when the book is opened the edges look like a pair of butterfly wings rather than being parallel along the tops and bottoms.

wipe-on-plate Litho plate to which the light-sensitive coating is applied by hand.

wire The moving fine mesh belt on which liquid stock is formed into a web of paper by draining away the water. **Wire side** is the side of the web which rests on the wire (also known as the **underside** or **wrong side**). **Wire mark** is the impression left by the wire on the web.

wire-binding or **wire-o binding** Binding method comprising a continuous double loop of wire running through slots in the margin of a book.

wire section That part of the Fourdrinier paper machine that contains the machine **wire**.

wire stitching See **saddle stitching**.

with the grain In the direction of the length of the original web. Paper folds more easily with the grain.

WOB White on black (i.e. reversed out).

wood-containing Referring to papers which are **part-mechanical** in furnish.

woodcut Hand engraving cut into a block of wood for print-making.

woodfree paper Full woodfree paper contains no **mechanical pulp** at all. This is sometimes known as **pure woodfree**. It is generally accepted, however, that woodfree paper may include up to 10% mechanical or other fibre and still fall within the definition of woodfree.

woodfree pulp Pulp which is processed chemically and which contains no mechanical **groundwood**.

wood pulp Pulp made from wood.

woodtype Typographical characters (usually in sizes over 72pt) made from wood. Often called **poster type**.

woof The cross threads in a woven material. Also, **weft**. Compare **warp**.

word As a computer term, a group of **bits** (q.v.) recognised by the computer as the smallest logical unit of information for processing. In micros, computer words may be eight, 16 or 32 bits in length (in ascending order of power).

Word A popular word processing package developed by Microsoft. Also, **MS Word**.

Illus 79. A woodcut from a book printed by Caxton in 1483.

word break Division of a word at a line ending.

word count facility The facility offered in some word processing systems to keep a log of the number of words keyed in at any one time.

WordPerfect A foremost word-processing package in both the Applemac and IBM PC environments. Its main competitors are WordStar, MS Word, MacWrite, WriteNow.

word processing The act of composing, inputting and editing text through the medium of a dedicated **word processor** or specific word processing software.

word processor Machine using computer logic to accept, store and retrieve documents for subsequent editing and output in typewriter style.

wordspace The variable space between words which may be increased or decreased to justify a line.

WordStar One of the first and still most popular proprietary word processing packages. It is associated especially with the IBM PC environment.

word wrap The automatic wrapping of text on to the next line in word-processing or other text setting when a line end is encountered.

work and back See **sheetwork**.

work and tumble Printing the reverse side of a sheet by turning it over on its long axis from gripper to back and using the same plate. Each sheet, cut in half, yields two copies.

work and turn Printing the first side of a sheet, turning the stack across its short axis, and then printing the reverse side of the sheet using the same plate and the same gripper edge. Each sheet, cut in half, yields two copies.

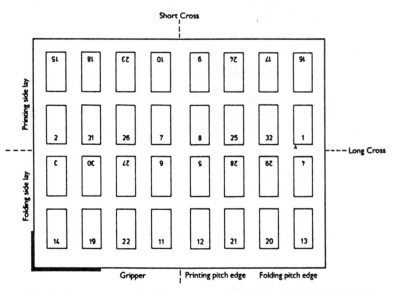

Illus 80. Work and turn: a forme of 32 pages to view which will be backed up with itself.

workings Number of **passes** through a printing machine to make up a complete job, e.g. four workings on a single-colour press to produce a four-colour print or one working on a four-colour press.

working sharp The deterioration of an image during a press run in which fine lines and highlight halftone dots become finer and then start to disappear. The opposite effect to that of a **thickening image**.

workstation Part of a computer typesetting system manned by an operator, e.g. an editing terminal.

work-up The unintentional lifting to impression level of spacing materials in a letterpress forme.

WORM Acronym for Write Once Read Many, an **optical digital disc** on which data can be recorded but not erased by the user.

worm A program introduced by a software publisher that is designed to abort execution if unauthorised usage is detected. Compare **virus**.

wove Paper produced using a plain, woven dandy roll and therefore without laid lines, as distinct from **laid paper** (q.v.).

woven material Genuine cloth, used for case covering. The two main qualities of woven cloth used for coverings are 'single-warp' and 'double-warp' buckram. In the case of single-warp buckram, the standard specification is '40/40', i.e. 40 strands of thread per linear inch in each direction.

wp Abbreviation for **word processor** or **word processing**.

wp format In word processing, a file format which contains all the printer control codes (soft carriage returns, etc) as opposed to an **ASCII** file format, which contains the words and spaces with other codes stripped out.

wpm Words per minute. Standard measure of copy-typing speed.

wrap Plate section placed around the outside of a folded text section in a book and bound in. Contrast **insert**.

wraparound A word processing facility that moves a word to a preceding or following line to avoid word breaks or to allow for deletion or insertion. Also called **word wrap**.

wraparound plate Thin letterpress printing plate which is clamped around the plate cylinder.

wrapping 1. Also called **wrappering**. Attaching a paper cover by gluing at the spine. See also **drawn-on cover**. 2. Inserting magazines into wrappers for mailing.

wrinkles 1. Creases in printed paper caused by uneven moisture absorption. 2. Uneven surface of ink during drying.

write To record or output electronic data.

write-black In laser printing, a write-black printer is one in which the laser exposes the black areas of an original, which then have toner applied to them to form the image on paper. Contrast the **write-white** printer, in which the laser exposes the white areas of the original, and toner is applied to what is left unexposed. Write-black printers tend to produce more printable solids, and leave less risk of specks – toner scatter – occurring in white areas.

write enable A means of allowing data to be written to magnetic disc or tape. With **floppy discs** this is achieved typically by the removal of an adhesive tab from the disc's write-protect notch while with magnetic tape the same objective is achieved by repositioning a sliding tab on a **cartridge** or **cassette** enclosure or by the replacement of a **file protect ring** on a reel of magnetic tape. Compare **write protect**.

write protect A means of preventing data being written to magnetic disc or tape. With **floppy discs** this is achieved typically by placing an adhesive tab over the disc's write-protect notch while with magnetic tape the same objective is achieved by repositioning a sliding tab on a **catridge** or **cassette** enclosure or by the removal of a **file protect ring** from a reel of magnetic tape. Compare **write enable**.

write-white See under **write-black**.

writings Papers sized for writing without ink spread.

wrong fount See **wf**.

wrong grain See **cross grain**.

wrong-reading Film which reads incorrectly, i.e. reversed from left to right, when viewed from the emulsion side. Also called **reverse-reading**.

wrong side See **underside, wire side**.

WSOP Web sized offset printing paper. A high-finish SC mechanical mainly used for magazines, but appropriate for some grades of book-work.

wysiwyg What you see is what you get. Acronym used to describe a visual display showing an exact replica of its output.

X, Y, Z

Xenix A version of the **Unix** operating system developed by Microsoft.

xenon flash Intense momentary light source used in photosetting.

xerography Electrostatic copying process in which toner adheres to charged paper to produce an image.

x-height Height of body of lower-case letters, exclusive of ascenders and descenders, i.e. height of the letter x.

x-line Alignment along the tops of lower-case letters. Also, **mean line** (q.v.).

XON-XOFF A data communications protocol which typically requires a **full duplex** link. When the receiving device is unable to accept further data it sends an **ASCII** XOFF character.

xx Mark indicating **retree** (q.v.).

xxx Mark indicating **broke** (q.v.).

yankee dryer Steam-heated paper drying cylinder generating a glazed finish.

yapp cover Binding material edges which overlap the case boards giving a 'fringed' effect. Often used for bibles.

yield In papermaking, yield is the term used to describe the quantity of one material derived from another in a sequence of processes. Thus the yield of finished **bleached softwood kraft** pulp from, say, 100 tonnes of woodchips might be 65-70 tonnes. In the most general terms, 1 **SRW** tree of the kind felled for pulp and papermaking, weighing perhaps 200Kgs, yields around 100Kgs of chemical woodpulp, which results in around 50Kgs of finished paper. This comes to around 150 books of average size.

Z80 Early 8-bit microprocessor chip for which the **CP/M** operating system was originally developed.

zinc engraving Relief engraving made on zinc and often used for short-run blocking in preference to a chemac. Also called zinco.

Zip-a-tone Proprietary name for patterned line or dot effects applied as rub-down film on to artwork. See also **Letraset, transfer type**.

zone In printing, an alternative term for **track** (q.v.).

z-tensile strength In papermaking, the internal bonding strength of a paper, determined by the quantity of **fillers** used in the furnish and the kind of fibre used. Boards or papers with low z-tensile strength can delaminate during printing.

The Blueprint
Dictionary of
Printing and
Publishing

Also by John Peacock:

BOOK PRODUCTION
THE PRINT AND PRODUCTION MANUAL (WITH BERRILL, BARNARD)

Also by Michael Barnard:

MAGAZINE AND JOURNAL PRODUCTION
INTRODUCTION TO PRINT BUYING
INSIDE MAGAZINES
MAKING ELECTRONIC MANUSCRIPTS
THE POCKET GLOSSARY OF ADVERTISING TERMS
THE POCKET GLOSSARY OF PRINTING, BINDING AND PAPER TERMS
THE POCKET GLOSSARY OF DESIGN AND TYPOGRAPHIC TERMS
THE PUBLISHER'S GUIDE TO DESKTOP PUBLISHING (WITH WILSON-DAVIES, ST. JOHN BATE)
THE PRINT AND PRODUCTION MANUAL (WITH PEACOCK, BERRILL)